Solomon

The **Bible Story**
Library

Solomon orders the infant to be cut in two

THE

BIBLE STORY

LIBRARY

The Holy Scriptures retold in story form for the young and as an explanation and commentary for all, based on traditional texts and illustrated with the most famous Biblical art.

VOLUME
III
From Solomon to the
Roman Conquest

Edited by TURNER HODGES
with the assistance of ELIZABETH MacLEAN
Designed and produced by DONALD D. WOLF
with the assistance of MARGOT L. WOLF
With many new illustrations in full color by RAFAELLO BUSONI

NEW YORK
EDUCATIONAL BOOK GUILD
1957

ACKNOWLEDGMENTS

THIS WORK HAS BEEN SUBMITTED to clergymen of all faiths, and the publishers and editors are most grateful for the uniformly favorable comment on its fidelity to the Scriptures. They wish especially to acknowledge the gracious commendation of the following:

The Rev. Father ALBAN BAER, O.S.B., of the Priory, Portsmouth, who scrutinized the full work from the standpoint of the Catholic reader.

The Rev. Dr. DANIEL S. POLING, Editor of *The Christian Herald,* who wrote, "What you have done will be, I think, universally acceptable to our churches."

The Rev. Dr. LEROY A. MARTIN, President of Tennessee Wesleyan College, who wrote, "I congratulate you on doing an outstanding job."

The Very Rev. JUVENAL D. LALOR, O.F.M., of Christ the King Seminary, then President of St. Bonaventure University, who graciously praised the faithful "but oh, so clear" presentation.

Rabbi EPHRAIM S. KOLATCH of Temple Beth-el, New York, who commended the publishers' "great service to our children in presenting the Bible stories in one of the most attractive fashions I have ever observed."

Contents

List of Color Illustrations

The Glory of Solomon the King, the Division into Two Kingdoms, the History of Israel and Judah, the Babylonian Captivity, and the Restoration of the Temple.

1

The story of Solomon and the gift of wisdom

 NDER KING DAVID THE ISRAELITES became truly a great nation, as God had promised their forefathers hundreds of years before. Fully nine million people lived in his country and served him. He lived in great splendor in his palace at Jerusalem, the capital. He had large armies and won many battles against the enemies who lived on the borders of his land. Some of these battles were won over the Philistines, in whose army there were giants like Goliath, whom David had killed as a youth.

As David grew old, he began to think about who would become king after him. Through the prophet Nathan he learned that God wished him to choose Solomon, the second son who was born to David and his wife Bathsheba. You may remember that Bathsheba was the woman whom David desired so much that he had her husband killed so that he could marry her.

David promised Bathsheba that her son Solomon would be the next king of the Israelites; but David had another son, named Adonijah, who also wanted to be king.

Adonijah held a great feast, to which he invited all his friends. At that feast he persuaded them that they should make him king over Israel, as soon as David died.

When David heard of this he determined to make certain that Solomon, and not Adonijah, would become king.

"Who knows what the people might do after I am dead?" he asked himself. "I will make Solomon king in my place while I am still alive."

David told his servants to take his own mule, place Solomon on its back, and go to a fountain called Gihon, near the city of Jerusalem. There they

Solomon becomes the king

were to anoint Solomon as king, and everyone should shout "God save King Solomon!" Trumpets would blow, and the sound of the celebration would be heard far and wide.

Then Solomon was to return to David's palace and sit on the throne, so that everyone would know that he was already the king over Israel.

Adonijah heard the trumpets and the people shouting "God save King Solomon!"

"What is the meaning of all that noise?" he asked.

"David has made Solomon king over Israel," he was told.

At that news Adonijah was terrified. He feared that Solomon would kill him. In those times a new king frequently executed all the people who had opposed him or who might have tried to become king themselves. But Solomon told Adonijah that he would be safe as long as he lived according to the laws of God.

David remained the actual ruler as long as he lived, but he died a few years later. He was seventy years old and had been king for nearly forty years. Solomon also was king for nearly forty years. Most of his reign was a happy one. His father had been king during a troubled and difficult time, but now the land was quiet and peaceful.

There was a time, during the first year or two of Solomon's reign, when there was violence and bloodshed. Adonijah did not keep his promise to live as a good man, and he was put to death. David's old captain, Joab, was also put to death, as was Shimei. Abiathar, the priest who had taken Adonijah's part, was sent away as punishment. Solomon could not bring himself to have Abiathar executed, because the priest had been a good friend to King David.

Now Solomon could reign without further trouble from his enemies within the land. His father David had taught him to keep the law of God, and Solomon tried earnestly to do what was right.

God speaks to Solomon in a dream

One night God spoke to Solomon in a dream and offered to give him anything he might ask for.

Solomon did not ask for wealth, or power, or even for good health.

"Lord," he prayed, "I am young, and I know very

Solomon, kneeling, is anointed king by the prophet Nathan.

little. Give me wisdom, so that I shall be able to teach the people of my land in a manner pleasing to the Lord. Let me know what is right, so that my judgments will be wise and good. I ask the gift of wisdom."

The Lord was pleased with Solomon. He promised Solomon that he not only would be very wise but also would be given great riches and honor—more than any other king before him or any that would come after him. Further, if Solomon lived by the commandments of the Lord, he would enjoy a long, full life.

Soon Solomon was given an opportunity to use the wisdom the Lord had granted him.

The women and the baby
One day two women appeared before Solomon to get his judgment. With them they carried a dead baby and a live, healthy baby, both of them boys. The two babies were about the same age.

One of the women explained the situation.

"We live in the same house," she said. "My baby is just three days older than this woman's baby was. Hers died during the night, and while I was sleeping, she took my baby from me, and placed the dead baby in my bed, so that I would think that my child had died. But when I looked at the dead infant, I knew immediately that it was not my son, but hers."

"That is a lie!" cried the other woman. "It was her son who died in the night, and this living child is mine!"

"Judge between us," they asked. "Decide which one should have the living child."

This was a difficult case to judge. How could Solomon know which woman was telling the truth?

"Bring out a large sword!" he commanded a servant. The sword was brought.

"Now, take the sword and divide the living child in two," ordered Solomon. "Then each woman may have one half of the baby and there will be no need for further argument."

"Oh, no!" immediately cried one of the women. "Let her have the baby!"

"Put down the sword," ordered Solomon. "The child will not be killed. Give the baby to the woman who was willing to let her rival have it, rather than to see it killed, for she is the real mother of the infant."

All the people of Israel heard of this judgment, and they all knew that the Lord had given Solomon his wisdom. They were happy that he was their king. (The frontispiece by Busoni illustrates this scene.)

Although Solomon was extremely wise, and knew many, many things, he was humble about his great wisdom. He knew that God had given it to him, and that he himself could not take the credit.

Solomon knew the different kinds of birds, fish, reptiles and animals that lived in the land. He knew the names of the trees and the flowers, and all the plants about him. He was given a greater wisdom, and a wider scope of general knowledge, than any other man alive. He knew more than the priests, or the wise men, or the teachers.

Solomon's writings Solomon was also a great writer. He wrote three thousand proverbs, or wise sayings, and five thousand songs. People still read his proverbs, for they are in the Bible.

The Book of Ecclesiastes, or The Preacher, written by Solomon, is another of the books of the Old Testament. The most beautiful of the songs written by Solomon is called "The Song of Songs," or "Song of Solomon." It is one of the most beautiful poems ever written, and it can be found in the Old Testament directly following the Book of Ecclesiastes. You can read more about these poetical writings on page 380 of this volume.

2

The story of the Temple at Jerusalem

W HEN MOSES LED THE ISRAELITES from Egypt to the Holy land, by God's command the people built a "house of God" in which to keep the Ark of the Covenant (that is the chest containing the Ten Commandments) and other holy things. They called this first house of God a tabernacle, or tent, because it could be packed up and carried from place to place as the people of Israel traveled.

Hundreds of years later, King David wanted to build a permanent house of God, or Temple, in his capital of Jerusalem. But God told David not to build it but to wait for his son Solomon to do so.

At length Solomon was ready to start building the great Temple to the Lord, in which the Ark of the Covenant would be kept. David, before he died, had given Solomon instructions for building the Temple.

At that time David had called the leaders of the people together. He told them he had given Solomon a great many precious materials to help build the Temple: brass, iron, precious stones, marble, and much gold and silver. Some of these things had been taken from enemies beaten in battle, and some of them were of David's own riches. David asked the people if they would like to contribute to the materials.

"Much is needed," he told them. "The walls must be covered with pure silver, and the vessels of the Temple are to be made of gold and silver."

Many of the people then brought gifts. They gave the Lord more gold, and silver, and brass, and precious stones.

David thanked the Lord for making himself and the people willing to give these gifts. To the people he said,

The Temple of Solomon. Upper left, the cedars of Lebanon are cut and transported on carts to the sea, where they are floated to Israel. Upper right, the laver or jar of Aaron, so called because the first one was made for Aaron, the first high priest; below it, the Ark of the Covenant. Next above, the building of the altar.

The Temple of Solomon. Above, the great building stones are dragged up Mount Zion to the top of the eastern hill of Jerusalem, Mount Moriah, where the Temple stood. Below, a representation of the Temple. There are various courts, used for different purposes. The Holy of Holies and Ark are in the tall central building.

369

"All that you have given is truly the Lord's; for the Lord gave you everything you have, and you have only given back to Him some part of it."

Now, when Solomon was about to start building the Temple, he had all the things that David had gathered before his death. There was still need for lumber, and for this Solomon went to Hiram, the king of Tyre, in whose land there were great forests. Hiram had always been a great friend of David's.

The cedars of Lebanon "I am glad to help you," Hiram told Solomon. "The cedar trees and the fir trees in the forests of Lebanon will be suitable for building parts of your temple. I will send my men to cut them for you, and take the logs to the sea. By sea the logs can be floated to the shores of your country and taken from there into Jerusalem."

To help the workmen of Hiram, Solomon sent many thousands of his own men to Lebanon. The men of the two countries worked together at cutting trees for lumber. Solomon sent gifts of grain, oil, and wine for Hiram's men.

Jerusalem in the time of Solomon, showing the Temple (square) and palace.

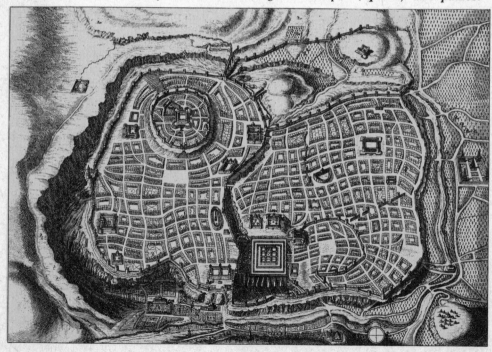

Dedication of Solomon's Temple, in the court outside the Holy of Holies.

The plan for the Temple had been given to David by the Lord. The building was to be one hundred feet long, thirty-three feet wide, and fifty feet high. This height did not include a steeple, or tower, which was to be two hundred feet high.

The Temple was very beautiful. It was made all of stone for strength, and the individual blocks of stone were cut and prepared some distance away, so that at no time while the Temple was under construction was there the sound of an iron tool striking against stone.

When the stones had all been set in place, the entire inside was covered with cedar wood, so that not one bit of stone could be seen on the inside walls. The cedar wood was beautifully carved and then was covered with thin sheets of pure gold, hammered and rolled out until it was like paper. There were many narrow windows in the walls of the temple. Outside the walls there were rooms for the priests to live in.

The Temple was planned to be like the tabernacle. The Ark of the Covenant and the Mercy Seat were to remain in the Temple permanently. Therefore, like the tabernacle, the Temple was divided into two separate

371

rooms by means of a beautiful curtain called the "veil." The curtain was made of blue, purple and crimson cloth. The inside room was called the Most Holy Place, because the Ark of the Covenant was to be kept there.

The walls on the inside of the Most Holy Place were covered with wood that had been carved to represent cherubim (angels), and palm trees, and flowers. These Solomon had covered with gold, and the floor as well. Two cherubim, each fifteen feet high, were carved out of olive wood, and Solomon had them covered with gold also. They stood facing each other, with their wings outspread and stretching from one wall to the other.

The altar of the Temple was made of brass. It was four times as large as the altar Moses had made for the tabernacle.

All of the other things that had been in the tabernacle were included in the equipment for the Temple. There were the golden candlesticks, the lavers or basins for water in which the priests must wash themselves before entering to offer sacrifices, the tables for the loaves of unleavened bread, and the censers in which the priests burned incense.

From the time the building of the Temple was started until it was finally completed, the people worked for more than seven years.

When the Temple was finished, there were ceremonies to dedicate it to the Lord. Solomon called all the elders and the chief men of Israel to Jerusalem to be present when the Ark was taken into the Temple. Only priests were permitted to touch the Ark, so the priests carried it into the Temple and placed it under the wings of the two cherubim, covered with gold, in the Most Holy Place.

The Lord comes in a cloud   When the priests had left the Ark in the Most Holy Place and had come out of the building, a great cloud filled the Temple. The cloud was the glory of God.

Then Solomon stood up before the people, and gave thanks to the Lord for helping them to build their Temple. He asked the Lord to accept it as His own. Then Solomon spoke aloud, praying to the Lord within the hearing of the people assembled before the temple.

"Please, Lord, hear and answer all the prayers that the people of Israel make in this house," said Solomon. "If ever they should sin so that the Lord would give their enemies victory over them—if they should sin and be punished by drought so that no rain would fall on their vines and their crops—if they should offend the Lord so that the Lord might punish them by sending pestilence and disease upon them, or by sending locusts or caterpillars to devour the grain—if ever these people should sin, may the good Lord forgive them when they come to this house and raise their voices in prayer."

There was an offering lying on the altar at this time, and when Solomon had finished speaking a fire came down from heaven and burned up the offering on the altar.

When the Israelites saw this, they bowed down and worshiped the Lord. "The Lord is with us," they cried. "His glory is with us forever!"

Then Solomon and the people all offered sacrifices. Solomon gave twenty-two thousand oxen and a hundred and twenty thousand sheep as a peace offering, and for fourteen days all the people feasted with the meats of the peace offering. A burnt offering was made to atone for sin, and the animal's flesh was all burned up, so that there was nothing left but charred bone. A peace offering, however, was made as a means of giving thanks, and the meat of the animals sacrificed was cooked and eaten in a feast.

During the night, the Lord spoke to Solomon and told him that the Temple was acceptable to the Lord. If the people of Israel sinned and repented of their sins, and visited the Temple to pray, the Lord would forgive the sins.

3

The story of the Queen of Sheba

SOLOMON WAS KING OVER ALL of Israel, and in many of the surrounding countries the people paid tribute, or taxes, to Solomon as long as he was king.

Twelve officers of Israel were responsible for providing all the food consumed by Solomon's enormous household. The daily supply of food that was used was huge. In a single day, they needed thirty oxen, a hundred sheep, and quantities of deer and fowl. Each of the twelve officers had charge of providing the food for one month of the year. They were expected also to supply feed and straw for the horses and camels that Solomon owned.

These vast quantities of food were not consumed by Solomon's personal family only, but the entire royal household, all its servants, all their families, and all the guests that visited them. The enormous size of the royal household can be indicated by the fact that Solomon had forty thousand horses alone, and twelve thousand horsemen to care for them.

When Solomon had completed the building of the Temple he built himself a beautiful palace and many other houses. He built many walled cities and many ships, so that he had a large navy. The ships of Solomon's navy sailed every year to distant lands and returned with great cargoes of all kinds of things that were not grown or produced in the land of Israel. They brought back gold and silver and ivory, and apes and peacocks.

Solomon made the heathen people of the land slaves while the men of Israel were soldiers and leaders.

The people of the distant lands visited by Solomon's ships were much impressed by the tales they heard of Solomon's riches and his great wisdom. Many made the journey to Jerusalem in order to see him and to hear his words of wisdom. When they came they brought with them valuable gifts of gold, silver, clothing, spices, horses, and mules.

As time went on, Solomon's riches increased. At length he had fourteen hundred chariots and two thousand drivers for them. All the dishes and vessels he used in his palace were made of gold, and his throne was of ivory covered with gold. Six steps led up to his throne, and on the steps were beautifully carved figures of lions. Solomon had treasures of all kinds.

Solomon's thousand wives

King Solomon had many wives. In all, there were seven hundred wives who were princesses, and three hundred concubines, or wives who were women of more lowly station, a total of one thousand. Some of these were women of the heathen nations, though men of Israel had long since been forbidden to marry into families of idol-worshipers. Solomon had disobeyed this command, in marrying women of the Ammonites, the Moabites, Edomites, Sidonians, and Hittites. He did this as an act of friendship with kings of neighboring nations and with the chiefs of cities and tribes in his own country. When he married a daughter or sister of a foreign king it made them related in a way and made it less likely that their countries would go to war against each other. Likewise, marrying into the families of Israelite leaders prevented rebellions against Solomon's rule. This policy helped Solomon to have a peaceful reign but it did not please the Lord, who had told all men of Israel not to marry heathens.

A distant land called Sheba was ruled by a queen, which was unusual in those times. The queen heard many tales of the wonders to be seen in Solomon's city of Jerusalem. She heard that this king was wiser than any other man and that he possessed riches beyond belief. The queen could not believe that all the stories she heard were true, but she decided that she would visit this fabulous king and see for herself. His riches were not especially important to the Queen of Sheba, for she also had great wealth; his knowledge of the true God was the matter that interested the queen.

With a large company of servants, guards, and attendants, the Queen of Sheba set out to visit Jerusalem. Dozens of camels were loaded with saddlebags containing spices, sandalwood, gold, and precious stones, as gifts to King Solomon, and the caravan entered Jerusalem in a fashion suitable to visiting royalty. Solomon made the queen welcome and showed her his great palace and all the buildings of his city.

The Queen of Sheba visits King Solomon: Gustave Doré's engraving.

The queen was a very intelligent woman and she asked many difficult questions of Solomon. In every case he answered her in a way that revealed his great wisdom. She was amazed at Solomon's knowledge and impressed with his wealth.

"Truly," she exclaimed, "I had believed that the travelers with whom I talked were making up stories about you and your wealth. Now, as I see it for myself, I realize that I did not hear half of the true story."

Solomon's wisdom and vast wealth did not impress the queen more than his righteousness.

"Your wives are fortunate to have such a husband," she said. "Your servants are fortunate to have such a master, from whom they can hear wisdom each day. The Lord must indeed be pleased with you."

Before the queen went back to her own home in Sheba, Solomon made many gifts to her. When the queen returned to her own land, her camels were as heavily loaded as when she had arrived in Israel, although she had been most generous in the gifts she gave Solomon.

There is no further reference to the Queen of Sheba in the Bible, but the people of Ethiopia trace their descent to her.

As the king grew older, his wives influenced him and persuaded him to adopt some of their idols as false gods. This displeased the Lord.

The Lord told Solomon that as a punishment for his turning away from the one true God, the kingdom of Israel would be taken away from his family. Solomon himself would be permitted to reign over the entire kingdom during his lifetime, for the sake of David, his father, but after Solomon's death the kingdom was to be divided, and only a small part of it would be ruled by Rehoboam, Solomon's son.

As Solomon grew older he was no longer made happy by his great wealth and all his beautiful possessions. It was at this time that he wrote the words that begin the book of Ecclesiastes in the Old Testament:

"Vanity of vanities, all is vanity! . . . vanity and vexation of spirit!"

4

The poetical books of the Bible

THE BIBLE IS MANY BOOKS in one; in fact, the word Bible does not mean "book" so much as it means "library."

Some of the books of the Bible are poetry. They are:

PSALMS
PROVERBS
ECCLESIASTES
SONG OF SONGS, or SONG OF SOLOMON

The book of Job is also a poetical book. It tells the story of a man named Job who was faithful to the Lord. No one can be sure when Job lived; he might have lived at any time and his story would be just as important.

Because many of the psalms, or hymns, were written by David, and much of the other poetry in the Bible is believed to have been written by David's son Solomon, a description of the poetical books is placed here, after the stories of their two reigns as kings in Israel. The Story of Job will follow.

The Psalms The Book of Psalms in the Bible consists of one hundred and fifty hymns, or poems in praise of the Lord. The word "psalm" means a song to be sung to the accompaniment of a stringed instrument.

Many of the psalms were intended to be sung in the worship at the Temple. Others were intended to be sung as prayers by the people. They all contain poetical expressions that sometimes make the meaning difficult to understand.

King David is credited with writing nearly half of the hundred and fifty psalms in the Book of Psalms. He may have written more than that. Asaph, the prophet, also wrote many of the psalms, and King Solomon is believed to have written some of them. In many instances the author is unknown. Some of the psalms of David prophesy things that had not yet occurred when they were written. The Messiah, or king, who would be sent by the Lord as the Saviour of men, is foretold in David's writings.

The Titles of the Psalms Some of the psalms are shown in the Bible with titles. Frequently the titles refer to times or places that are connected with things that happened to David. For example, the title may explain that David wrote the psalm as a prayer and expression of faith while he was fleeing from his son Absalom, or that he wrote the psalm in thanksgiving and praise when the Lord delivered him from King Saul and other enemies.

The titles of some psalms tell what instruments are to be used as an accompaniment; for example, *neginoth,* a kind of stringed instrument similar to the lyre or lute, or *nehiloth,* a wind instrument similar to the flute. In a few cases, the titles of the psalms include words whose meaning is not entirely clear to Bible scholars.

Alphabetical Psalms Some psalms are divided into twenty-two parts each. There were twenty-two letters in the Hebrew alphabet, and in these psalms the first verse or stanza begins with the first letter of the Hebrew alphabet, the second verse or stanza begins with the second letter, and so on through the twenty-second. Some translators of the Bible into English have followed this style, using the first twenty-two letters of the English alphabet.

The Psalms of degrees Some psalms are headed "a song of degrees," or "a gradual canticle," or "a song of ascents." These mean the same thing. In some of the sacred services of the Levites, the men climbed a series of steps. They *ascended* the steps *gradually,* or *by degrees.* The psalms of degrees were apparently intended to be sung in sections, one for each step.

Although most of the psalms in the Bible are found in the Book of Psalms, there are some in other books.

After the people of Israel had crossed the Red Sea safely, and the waters had closed on the pursuing Egyptian army, they celebrated and gave

*"The Lord [God] said unto my Lord [Christ], Sit thou at my right hand
. . ." A Psalm quoted by Jesus. A Holbein engraving* (see opposite page).

thanks to the Lord. On this occasion, Moses' sister Miriam sang a beautiful
psalm of thanks and praise to the Lord, and the people sang with her. This
is in Chapter 15 of Exodus. Another beautiful psalm was that of Moses,
spoken to the people of Israel shortly before his death. This can be found in
Chapter 32 of Deuteronomy.

The Proverbs   The Book of Proverbs consists of wise sayings of King
Solomon. The sayings themselves do not start until the
tenth chapter of Proverbs. Before that, there is an introduction and an explanation of what is to follow.

Ecclesiastes   The Book of Ecclesiastes in the Old Testament is believed to have been written by King Solomon. It ex-
presses his feeling that life on earth is never truly good and satisfying to
the soul. The words "Vanity of vanities, all is vanity," which begin Ecclesiastes, mean that all earthly struggles for success and happiness are "in
vain," or futile.

Solomon was a very rich man and knew many earthly pleasures. He does

"The fool has said in his heart, There is no God." Like the picture on the opposite page, this is from a famous engraving by Hans Holbein the Younger.

not say that pleasures are undesirable, or that one should not enjoy life, but he points out that after the change that is called death everyone will leave behind all earthly riches and will go on to another kind of life, where only things of the spirit are of any consequence.

Song of Solomon

The Song of Songs is a beautiful poem written by King Solomon. It is believed to describe the relationship between the Church and Christ. It is in the form of an allegory, which means that although it appears to describe one thing, it really uses that thing as a symbol of another. For example, the words "wife" and "bride" are used as symbols of the Church. The words "bridegroom" and "husband" are used as symbols of the Christ.

While reading the Song of Songs, one should always remember that the expressions of admiration for the beauty of the bride really mean admiration for the wonderful things about the Church of God. Where admiration for the bridegroom or husband is expressed, it should be understood to mean love and admiration for the virtues of Christ.

5

The story of Job

IN THE LAND OF UZ, one of the small countries peopled by the Israelites, there lived a very good man named Job. He was always careful to do the will of God. Job had seven sons and three daughters, whom he loved dearly. He was a very rich man and owned three thousand camels, seven thousand sheep, a thousand oxen, and five hundred asses. He had many servants, both men and women. He was the richest man in the part of the land where he lived.

His sons were grown up and had homes of their own. They often held feasts—first in one son's house, and then in another, taking turns. They always invited their three sisters to enjoy these feasts with them.

After the feasts were over, Job always spoke to them. Each time he said the same thing.

"If you have done any evil thing, repent of it," he warned them. "Offer up a burnt offering to the Lord for any evil you may have done." And then Job himself would offer up a burnt offering for each of his children, for fear they might have sinned in some fashion and displeased God.

Job enjoyed his riches and his blessings for a great many years; but then the Lord sent him trouble to test his patience and to see if Job's love of the Lord would survive great misery.

First God took away Job's great riches and made him a very poor man.

One day a messenger came to Job.

"While your oxen were plowing in the field, and the herd of asses was grazing beside them, a great band of robbers came and drove them all away," said the messenger. "Not only did they steal all of your oxen and asses, but they killed all your servants who were there, except me."

Job hears that disasters have taken away his wealth and loved ones.

Just as this servant finished speaking, another ran up to Job.
"A great fire fell out of the sky and burned up your sheep," he exclaimed. (It was probably what we would call lightning.) "Not only are all your sheep dead, but all the shepherds who were tending them are dead also. I am the only one left."

383

Hardly had this servant spoken when a third one ran to Job and gave him still more bad news.

"Some enemies have stolen your camels and have killed the servants who were taking care of them. I am the only one who escaped."

Then Job realized that in this short space of time he had lost all his great wealth. But even more tragic news was to come. A fourth servant came up to Job, and spoke.

"All your sons and daughters were enjoying a feast at the house of your eldest son, when suddenly a great wind blew over the house. The wind was so strong that it blew the house down completely. All who were inside are dead, except me. I escaped and came to tell you."

Job was filled with grief for his beloved children, but he bowed down to the earth and worshiped the Lord.

"I had nothing of my own when I was born into this world, and I shall have nothing of my own when I die and leave it," said Job. "It was God who gave me my riches and my children. Now God has taken them away from me. God knows what is best for me, and I thank Him for all that He has done for me."

Job's wife disputes his faith

God had further tests for Job's patience. Job next began to suffer from sickness and pain. He was covered from head to foot with painful boils, and he was seated on the ground suffering severe pain when his wife came out and spoke to him.

"Do you still trust in God?" she demanded angrily. "By now you should know that you are foolish to do so. Stop praising God as you do. Look at the trouble He has given you!"

But Job rebuked his wife.

"You are speaking foolishly," he said. "We have had so many good things from God that we should not complain if now we have some evil things."

So Job continued to worship the Lord and accepted God's will without question.

Three of Job's friends heard of his trouble and came to visit him, to offer him comfort. He had changed so much because of his suffering that they did not recognize him at first. They wept when they saw him. They thought he must have committed some dreadful sin for which God was punishing him.

"If you have done something wicked, do not do it again," they begged him. "Perhaps you took something that did not belong to you. Perhaps you were unkind to the poor. Perhaps you failed to pray to God. Repent of your sins, whatever they may be, and the Lord will forgive you."

Job knew he had not done any of the things his friends mentioned.

"You came here to comfort me," he said. "What you have been telling me does not comfort me at all. I did not send for you. If you had the kind of trouble I have, I would not be so unkind as to tell you you were wicked and sinful."

Job then spoke of his sorrow.

"The Lord has sent me great misery," he said. "I wish He would allow me to die, and suffer no longer. I cannot find rest at night. Often I have such pain I cannot sleep at all, and if I fall asleep for a few moments I have dreadful dreams. If someone would only pray to God for me! He does not seem to listen any more to my prayers.

Job, afflicted by boils, debates the goodness of God with his three friends: Photograph of a famous painting by the French artist Jean Bourdichon.

Yet I know that He is there, and I must suffer if God wills it."

The Lord did not let Job die and the Lord did not ease his pain. After a time, Job realized that he must go on suffering indefinitely, and he began to complain. He said that God was indeed cruel to him.

Instead of trying to encourage him, his three friends still insisted that he must have offended God.

"Your troubles are a punishment," they said. "God does not punish the

385

good. You must have done something very wicked, to deserve such punishment!"

The voice
of God
is heard

Job became angry at this, and soon he and his three friends were quarreling violently. All of them said things that they should not have said. Then Job heard a voice speaking out of a whirlwind that suddenly appeared. It was the voice of God.

God's voice told Job of the wonderful things that God had done. It was He who had made the earth, the sea, and the sky. It was God who sent the rain on the fields, to make grass and flowers spring up. He covered the rivers with ice, the ground with snow. He sent lightning from the sky. He gave wild beasts their food and fed the young birds that cried to Him when they were hungry. He gave beautiful feathers to the peacock and the ostrich. He made the horse that was swift and strong and He taught the eagle to fly.

When Job was reminded of all these things, he was asked by the voice if he could do them also, and whether he thought himself wise enough to teach God what He should do.

At this Job realized that he had sinned in complaining about what God had done to him. He prayed for forgiveness, for he had spoken of things he did not understand—things that were the affair of God and not of man.

Then God rebuked Job's three friends for speaking unkindly to a man in trouble. He told them to make a burnt offering of seven bullocks and seven rams and to ask Job to pray for them. They did as the Lord commanded, and Job prayed for them. The Lord granted Job's prayer for his friends, and they were forgiven.

Job is
blessed
again

Then the Lord took away Job's pain and illness. All of his brothers, sisters, and friends came to see him, and they had a feast. Each one gave him a bit of money and a gold earring. The Lord blessed Job even more fully than before he had suffered and made Job even richer than ever before. Job now had fourteen thousand sheep, six thousand camels, two thousand oxen, and a thousand asses. He also had seven more sons and three more daughters, and in all the land there were no more beautiful women than Job's daughters. When Job died, a hundred and forty years later, he was a very, very old man and a very happy and blessed one.

Accusation of Job by one of his three friends

The prophet Elijah is fed by ravens

6

The story of the two kingdoms

MONG THE PEOPLE OF ISRAEL was an industrious and able young man named Jeroboam. He was the son of one of Solomon's women servants, a widow named Zeruiah. Jeroboam's father was Nebat, one of the Ephraimites, a tribe of Israel.

One day as Jeroboam was walking outside Jerusalem, he met a prophet named Ahijah and Ahijah stopped him. The prophet was wearing a new cloak. He took off his cloak and tore it into twelve pieces. He then spoke to Jeroboam, to explain why he did so.

"Take ten of these pieces of my cloak," he said. "The Lord God of Israel is going to divide the kingdom. While King Solomon is still living, he will remain as ruler, because the Lord promised this to David, Solomon's father. But after the death of Solomon, his son will not rule in his place. Only a small part of the kingdom of Israel will remain under the rule of the house of David."

"But what do the ten pieces of your cloak mean?" asked Jeroboam.

"The Lord has said that you are to be king over ten of the tribes of Israel," said Ahijah the prophet.

When Solomon learned of what had been prophesied he attempted to kill Jeroboam, but the young man fled to Egypt, where he remained safely until he heard of Solomon's death.

Solomon had reigned as king of Israel for forty years. At length he died and his son Rehoboam became king.

Jeroboam returned to Jerusalem after Solomon's death. He was the leader of a large group of people who approached Rehoboam, the new king.

"Your father, King Solomon, made many harsh laws and ruled over us very sternly. He was often cruel. If you will treat us in a more kindly fashion, we will be happy to serve you as our king," they said.

"This is a matter that I must consider carefully," said Rehoboam. "Come back in three days and I will tell you what I decide to do."

Rehoboam then consulted some of his father's old friends.

"Do you think I should do as they ask?" he inquired.

"Yes, we do," was the advice of the men. "Treat the people of the land kindly and they will always be loyal to you."

Rehoboam was not satisfied to take the advice of the older men. He spoke next to some of the young men with whom he had grown up.

"Do you think I should deal more gently with the people than my father did?" he asked. "They think my father's laws were too harsh."

"Indeed not!" said the young men. "Treat them sternly, rule them firmly. Be more harsh even than your father was."

This was foolish advice, but Rehoboam decided to accept it.

When the three days were up, the people returned to hear Rehoboam's

Ahijah tells Jeroboam to tear his cloak, and prophesies his becoming king.

Rehoboam consults his father's friends: Engraving by Hans Holbein the Younger.

reply. He spoke to them very rudely.

"You think that my father's rule was harsh?" he cried. "My rule will be even more harsh! You found his punishments too severe? Mine will be far more severe than his! That is my answer to you!"

The people were extremely angry. They said nothing to Rehoboam, but after they left him they talked among themselves.

"The son of Solomon shall not rule over us!" they declared. "Our king shall be Jeroboam instead."

Ten of the tribes of Israel then joined together and made Jeroboam their king. Only the tribes of Judah and Benjamin remained with Rehoboam. In this way the Lord fulfilled the prophecy of Ahijah, and the kingdom of Israel was divided.

As soon as Rehoboam learned what had happened he sent a messenger to the ten tribes to urge them to return and be his subjects. Not only did the tribes refuse, but they killed Rehoboam's messenger.

News of the messenger's death soon reached Jerusalem, and the king was extremely angry. He gathered an army of the men of Judah and Benjamin, preparing to go out to battle against the rebellious ten tribes.

There were one hundred and eighty thousand soldiers of the king ready to fight against the tribes of Jeroboam, but a prophet named Shemaiah stopped them. The Lord had let Shemaiah know that this battle must not be.

"The Lord does not want you to go and fight against your brothers, for this is wrong," Shemaiah told the soldiers. "The Lord has told me that you are all to return to your homes."

The soldiers of Judah and Benjamin listened to the words of the prophet. All returned to their homes.

At this point, therefore, there were two kings reigning over the people of Israel. The kingdom ruled by Jeroboam was called the Kingdom of Israel, and the kingdom ruled by Rehoboam was called the Kingdom of Judah. The Kingdom of Israel was the northern kingdom, and the Kingdom of Judah was the southern kingdom.

After the division of the kingdom, the Israelites never again became a single nation. The Kingdom of Israel survived for about two hundred and nine years, and the Kingdom of Judah for about three hundred and forty-four years. During that time there were many kings, in both lands, and occasionally one king felt he was stronger than the other, and made war in an attempt to reunite the people of the two kingdoms under his own rule. These attempts were never successful and the Israelites remained divided.

7

The story of Jeroboam and the prophet

HE MEN OF THE TEN TRIBES who followed Jeroboam returned to their homes from Jerusalem, after they had rejected Rehoboam. Jeroboam was afraid that if his people went back to Jerusalem each year, to worship in the Temple there, they would turn against him eventually and take Rehoboam as their king.

"When that day comes, they will surely kill me," he decided. "The only thing to do is give them temples far from Jerusalem."

He did not tell the people of his fears. He pretended that it was too far for them to travel. "The distance to Jerusalem is great," he said. "I will build temples for you in the lands belonging to your own tribes."

Jeroboam then made two golden calves for the people to worship as gods, and built temples for them at the cities of Bethel and Dan, which were in different sections of the land belonging to the ten tribes.

"Here are your gods," he told the people. "These are the gods that brought your fathers out of Egypt, and gave you this land."

The people were quite satisfied to worship the golden idols, and Jeroboam took it upon himself to lead them still further away from the worship of the one true God. He instituted feasts, saying that he was following ancient tradition because they were like the feasts that the Lord had ordered to be observed by the people of Israel long before, in the time of Moses. Actually they were heathen feasts, but most of the Israelites in his kingdom celebrated them willingly.

One day Jeroboam was burning incense before one of the altars he had built to the false gods. This altar was in Bethel. While Jeroboam was standing there, a prophet of the Lord walked up to him. He had come all the way from the Kingdom of Judah at the Lord's command.

"On this very spot a true man of God will one day stand," the prophet

391

said. "The man's name will be Josiah, and he will destroy your idols and your altars."

Jeroboam was very angry, but he did not believe the prophet.

"You do not believe me," the prophet said. "To convince you, the Lord will send a sign this very day. This entire altar will shatter and all the ashes in it will pour out."

Jeroboam was filled with rage and he reached forth his hand, pointing at the man, and commanded his attendants to arrest him. "Seize this stranger, and take him away!" he ordered.

Jeroboam's hand is paralyzed

As he spoke his hand became stiff and useless and he could not even draw it back. At the same time, the altar split open and all the ashes poured out.

Jeroboam was frightened. He begged the man of God to pray to the Lord to restore the use of the withered hand. The holy man did so, and Jeroboam's hand was made normal again.

"Come home to eat and drink with me," begged Jeroboam.

"No, I cannot do that," said the stranger. "The Lord commanded me neither to eat nor to drink."

With that the man turned away, and set out for his home.

Living in Bethel at that time was a very old prophet who had dutifully served the Lord. He heard of the holy man from Judah, and he rode after him to catch up with him. He lied to the holy man, because he was so anxious to entertain a great man in his house.

"I, too, am a prophet of the Lord," he said. (This much was true.) "An angel of the Lord appeared to me and told me that you would be permitted to eat and drink in my house. Please come with me."

The Judean believed these false words and was persuaded to return and eat bread and drink water, which the Lord had forbidden him to do.

The Judean prophet soon set out again for his own country, but along the way a lion attacked him and killed him. It did not harm the ass on which he was riding, and it did not devour his body. The lion had been sent by the Lord to kill the man in punishment for his disobedience.

Soon afterward Abijah, the son of Jeroboam, became very ill.

"Disguise yourself," Jeroboam said to his wife, "and go to Shiloh, where Ahijah the prophet has his home. If you are disguised, no one will know that you are my wife. Ask Ahijah if our son will recover."

The disobedient Judean prophet is killed by a lion.

Ahijah sees through the disguise

Ahijah was a very old man by then, and his eyesight was poor. He probably would not have known that it was Jeroboam's wife who came to him, but the Lord had told him that she was coming. The old man heard the sound of her footsteps as she entered his house.

"Come in, wife of Jeroboam," he said. "Why are you pretending to be someone else? The Lord has told me of your coming."

"Then you know why I am here?" the woman asked.

"Yes," said Ahijah. "And I have sad news for you. The Lord is angry at your husband, Jeroboam, because he has shown no gratitude to the Lord who made him king of Israel."

"But my son, who is sick!" exclaimed Jeroboam's wife.

"He will die," said Ahijah. "But it is better that he should die now, for he has still some love of the true God left."

The wife of Jeroboam went home and told her husband what Ahijah had said. As soon as she reached her house, the son, Abijah, died. A few years later Jeroboam died also, after reigning for twenty-two years.

8

The story of Ahab and the prophet Elijah

THE NEXT FIVE KINGS OF the northern kingdom, the kingdom of Israel, in which the ten tribes lived, were evil men. They worshiped idols and they fought wars and killed their rivals so that they could be kings.

Nadeb, son of Jeroboam, reigned only two years. He was killed by Baasha, a chief of the tribe of Issachar (one of the Twelve Tribes of Israel). Baasha also killed all the other members of Jeroboam's family, which fulfilled the prophecy of the holy man God had sent to Jeroboam.

Baasha ruled for twenty-four years. His son Elah came after him, but Elah was killed because three military leaders, named Zimri and Omri and Tibni, were ambitious to become king. Of these rulers we remember Omri best, because he built the city of Samaria and for the next two hundred years—as long as the kingdom of Israel lasted—the city of Samaria was its capital.

Ahab was the son of Omri and became king after Omri died. All six of the previous kings of Israel had been wicked, but Ahab, the seventh king, was worse than any before him. Not only did he commit all the sins of idolatry, but he married a woman who was the daughter of a heathen king; he made her queen, with great power; and he allowed himself to be influenced by her evil ways. Her name was Jezebel.

Jezebel worshiped the heathen god Baal, and she persuaded Ahab to build a temple to Baal in the city of Samaria. The people were made to worship Baal with them, and the Lord became very angry. He decided that Ahab must be punished, and He sent a prophet to warn the king.

There were still some good people in Israel who lived according to

Elijah is fed by ravens (see also Busoni's color rendition, page 383).

God's laws, although Ahab and Jezebel made it difficult for them to do so. One of these good people was a holy prophet named Elijah. This was the man the Lord sent to Ahab.

"The Lord has told me to speak with you," Elijah said to the king, "and tell you that from now on there will be no more rain in the land of Israel until I, Elijah, ask the Lord to send it."

At once, Ahab wanted to kill Elijah, but the Lord had made provision to keep Elijah safe. Elijah was instructed to go to a certain brook, east of the Jordan River, and conceal himself there. The waters of the brook would satisfy the prophet's thirst, and God would provide him with food.

Elijah
is fed
by ravens

Elijah did as he was told. The water of the brook was sweet to drink, and each day the Lord sent ravens carrying food for Elijah. They flew down each morning and evening and carried bread and meat for Elijah to eat.

Although Ahab sent men to search for Elijah in every part of the land, they failed to find him, because the Lord protected the prophet.

Jezebel then decided that she was going to get rid of all the other prophets of the Lord, because they refused to worship Baal. She gave orders for them all to be killed.

But the chief minister of the king was a good man named Obadiah, and Obadiah hid a hundred of the Lord's prophets in caves and kept them provided with food and water.

As the Lord had predicted through Elijah, there was no more rain in the land of Israel. Crops failed everywhere, famine set in, and the people were hungry. Even the brook that supplied Elijah's water dried up, because there was no rain to water the springs from which it came.

Elijah was both hungry and thirsty, but he trusted in the Lord to provide for him and soon the Lord spoke to him. Elijah was told that he should go to the city of Zarephath, where the Lord had selected a widow to provide him with food.

Elijah went to Zarephath, where he saw the woman gathering sticks for her fire.

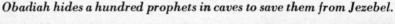

Obadiah hides a hundred prophets in caves to save them from Jezebel.

"I beg you," he said, "bring me a cup of water, for I am very thirsty."

The woman started after the water, and Elijah spoke again.

"And please, will you bring me a bit of bread also?" he asked.

"I swear to you, I have no bread," she answered. "I have only a small amount of flour and a little oil. I was gathering sticks to burn so that I could bake it for my son and myself, for we are hungry."

"You need have no fear," said Elijah. "The Lord has said that no matter how little flour and oil there is, it will last until the famine is over. Please do as I say. Bake me a small cake, and then return and bake more for yourself and your son. You will not lack for food."

Miracles of Elijah

The woman did as Elijah had told her, and the Lord made her flour and oil last for more than a year. She and her son and Elijah did not starve during the famine.

At the end of the first year, the woman's son became ill and died. In her grief, the woman turned on Elijah.

"Why has this happened?" she cried. "You came here only to remind me that I have sometimes sinned in my lifetime, and to kill my son!"

"Give me your son," said Elijah, and the woman did so.

Elijah carried the boy upstairs and prayed to the Lord. The Lord granted Elijah's prayer and allowed the boy to live again. When Elijah carried the living child downstairs and placed him in his mother's arms, she spoke in awe and gratitude.

"Now I know indeed that you are a true man of God," she said. "Whatever you say, it is the Lord who gives you the words to speak."

When Elijah had stayed for a little more than two years at the house of the widow and her son, the Lord told him to go to Ahab. The next day the Lord would send rain.

At about the same time Ahab, desperate because of the famine in his country, was speaking to his chief minister, Obadiah.

"You and I must go out and look for brooks or springs of water," Ahab said to Obadiah. "We will go in different directions. Perhaps we will find enough grass and water to keep our animals alive for a time."

With that Ahab and Obadiah set out, in different directions, each traveling alone. Obadiah met Elijah along the way.

"Can it be that you are here!" he exclaimed.

"Yes, it is I," said Elijah. "Go and tell King Ahab that Elijah is here."

"I cannot!" said Obadiah. "Do you not know that Ahab has looked for you everywhere, to kill you? The Lord did not let him find you, and now if I go to Ahab, surely the Lord will hide you again. Then when Ahab comes, you will have disappeared and Ahab will be angry with me. He will kill me!"

"No, he will not," said Elijah. "I promise you that I will be here when you come back with Ahab."

Ahab and Elijah meet
Obadiah then went to Ahab and brought him back to where Elijah was waiting. When the king saw the man he had been seeking for so long, he spoke angrily.

"So you are the man who has caused all the trouble in the land of Israel!" said Ahab.

"No, I am not," said Elijah. "You and your people have brought it upon yourselves, because you have forsaken the true God and worshiped Baal."

Then Elijah told Ahab what must be done.

"Go and assemble all the priests of Baal whom your wife honors by letting them eat at your table," said Elijah. "Take them to Mount Carmel, and let the rest of the people assemble there also, so that they may see what happens."

Ahab did so. When the priests and the people were assembled, Elijah spoke to them.

"How long will you continue in this foolish manner?" he asked them. "There can be only one God. If it is the Lord, who is my God, then you should obey Him. If it is Baal, then you should obey him. Let us find out which it is!

"I am the only prophet of the Lord left in this land," Elijah continued. "All the others have been killed, or forced to flee for their lives. But here are four hundred and fifty priests of Baal!

"Bring the bullocks, and let the prophets of Baal choose one of them, and kill it, and set it upon the altar of Baal. Do not put any fire under it. I will kill the other one and set it on the Lord's altar. I will not put any fire under my sacrifice, either. Then the priests of Baal can pray to Baal, and ask their god to send down fire from heaven, to burn the sacrifice. I will do the same, and pray to the Lord. Whichever is answered will decide which is the true God."

The people agreed that this was a fair test. The priests of Baal prepared the bullock that they had selected and placed it upon their altar. From morning till noon they called upon their god Baal to send down fire and burn the offering, but nothing happened.

Elijah mocked them at noontime.

"Call him more loudly," he said. "Remember, he is a god, and may be talking to someone, so that he cannot hear you. Perhaps he is off on a journey, or perhaps he is asleep, and you must call more loudly to awaken him!"

The priests of Baal did a heathen dance around the altar, as was their custom, but still no fire came. They cut themselves and each other with knives until the blood flowed, which was another heathen custom to persuade idols to answer prayers, but still no fire came.

Then Elijah built an altar of twelve stones, and put wood on the altar, and placed the other bullock on the wood.

"Now," he said to the people, "fill four barrels with water and pour the water over the wood and the offering."

The people were amazed, because they knew that wet wood is far more difficult to light than dry wood, but they did as Elijah said. He had them fill the barrels again and pour that water over the altar and its sacrifice, and then again for the third time. By this time the water had drenched the wood and the bullock.

Then, at the time when the Lord's priests were accustomed to offer up a lamb as a burnt offering each day, Elijah prayed.

"Lord, hear me, and send down fire."

God sends fire from the sky

With that, the fire of the Lord came down from heaven. It burned up the bullock and the wood and dried up all the water surrounding the altar.

When the people saw this they fell to the ground in fear, and cried out, "It is the Lord! The Lord is God!"

The Elijah said to the people,

"Capture the prophets of Baal! Do not let a single one of them escape!"

The people obeyed, and Elijah put the priests of Baal to death, for it was the Lord's command that all who deserted him to worship idols must die.

Elijah told Ahab to go to a little town nearby to eat and drink.

Elijah has the wood on the altar wetted before calling down the fire.

"The famine will soon be over," said Elijah. "The rain will come soon." Ahab went away as Elijah had said, and Elijah himself went to the top of Mount Carmel to pray for the rain that he knew God would send. After he had prayed, he spoke to his servant.

"Go and look out toward the sea," he said.

The servant went, but returned soon to say that he had seen nothing.

"Go seven times more," said Elijah, and the servant obeyed. After the seventh time, he told Elijah that he had seen something. "A little cloud is rising out of the sea, no larger than a man's hand," he reported.

"The Lord is sending rain," said Elijah. "Go and warn Ahab that he must hurry down from the mountain before the rain causes a deluge that will keep him from traveling."

The servant told Ahab what Elijah had said, and Ahab returned to the city of Jezreel in his chariot.

The little cloud grew larger and larger, and finally all the sky was black with clouds, and the rain fell in torrents.

9

The story of the calling of Elisha

WHEN AHAB TOLD HIS WIFE, Jezebel, what Elijah had done and how he had killed the prophets of Baal Jezebel was very angry. Swiftly she sent Elijah a message.

"By this time tomorrow, I will have had you put to death," the message said. "If for any reason I fail, then I pray that my gods may kill me instead!"

Elijah was frightened and fled to the city of Beersheba, which was in the land of Judah, south of Israel. He did not stop there, but the next day he traveled on deep into the desert to hide from his enemies.

There he seated himself under a tree and prayed to the Lord that he might die. Elijah was tired of running from those who wanted to kill him.

Elijah fell asleep under the tree, and as he slept an angel of the Lord came to him and touched him lightly to awaken him.

"Wake up, Elijah," said the angel. "Wake up and have something to eat."

When Elijah looked, he saw that there was a cake that had been baked on coals of fire next to where he had been sleeping, and beside the cake was a flask of water. Elijah ate the cake and drank the water, then fell asleep again.

The angel of the Lord appeared again and awakened him.

"You must get up now, and eat," the angel said. "You are going to make a long journey, and you will need the food to give you strength for it."

Elijah obeyed the angel, and set out on a journey toward Mount Horeb. For forty days and forty nights he traveled, and the food the Lord had provided gave him strength to go the whole distance without eating again.

When Elijah reached Mount Horeb, he went into a cave on the mountain and slept. The Lord spoke to him as he slept and asked him what he was doing there.

Elijah is fed by an angel of the Lord: A Doré engraving.

"The people of Israel no longer obey the laws of God," answered Elijah. "I am the only one who is left, and they are trying to kill me as well."

Suddenly, outside of the cave, there was a powerful wind. It tore up the side of the mountain and shattered great rocks. The wind was followed by a violent earthquake, and the earthquake was followed by a fire. When the fire was gone, Elijah heard a soft, gentle, and wonderful voice. He knew that it was the voice of God, and that God was there. Elijah covered his face, because he knew that no man could look at God. Then God told him to step out to the opening of the cave, and Elijah did so.

Once again the Lord asked Elijah what he was doing there, and once again Elijah answered as he had before.

Then the Lord informed Elijah that there were still seven thousand faithful Israelites who had never forsaken the true God to worship Baal. He told Elijah to go back to Jezreel, and along the way he would see the man whom God had chosen to do the work of the Lord after Elijah's death. Elijah was a very old man, and would not be able to remain on earth for many years longer.

Elijah went back to Jezreel, as the Lord had commanded, and as he was traveling he saw a young man plowing a field with his oxen. This was the man the Lord had chosen to carry on Elijah's work, and Elijah walked up to him.

Saying nothing, Elijah placed his cloak over the other man's shoulders, and the Lord gave the younger man—whose name was Elisha—the ability to understand what the act meant.

To wear a man's cloak, in those days, was nearly the same in significance as the modern saying, "to step into someone's shoes," meaning to take his place when he leaves.

"I will come with you!" exclaimed Elisha. "But wait while I go and kiss my parents goodbye."

Soon the younger man returned. Elisha followed Elijah and became his assistant, one day to inherit his position as a holy prophet of the Lord.

10

The story of Ahab and Benhadad

THE KING OF SYRIA WAS NAMED Benhadad, and he wanted the riches of Ahab in Israel. He gathered together a great army and set out to capture the city of Samaria, where Ahab lived. He did not try to surprise Ahab, but sent word ahead to tell him what was going to happen.

"I am coming to take your silver and gold, and all your treasures," said Benhadad's message. "I shall take your wives and your children also, to be my slaves."

Ahab was afraid and answered in a most cowardly fashion.

"Take all these things, if you will," said Ahab. "I will not stop you."

Then Benhadad sent another message. He had become more greedy.

"The things I named before are not enough," said Benhadad's message. "I will send my soldiers to your palace, and they will take everything you value most."

Ahab asked the elders of Israel what he should do.

"You should not allow Benhadad to do as he threatens!" said the elders.

When Benhadad heard what the elders had said, he sent another message to Ahab. He warned the king of Israel that he had a great army and would capture the city of Samaria.

"Do not boast of a victory you have not yet won!" was Ahab's answer to this message.

That irritated Benhadad, and he told his soldiers to get ready for battle immediately.

Then the Lord sent a prophet to Ahab, and told him not to fear.

"The Lord said that you should go against the Syrians with an army of only seven thousand men," said the prophet.

Ahab did as the prophet advised him and led his army into the field against the Syrians.

It so happened that Benhadad and his captains were at that time in a state of drunkenness in their tents. When Ahab's army attacked, the Syrians fled and Benhadad escaped on horseback with some of his cavalrymen.

This was not the end of Ahab's trouble with Benhadad. A year later Benhadad was persuaded to try again. He assembled an army as large as the one he had mustered in the previous year and set out to attack Samaria.

The people of Israel had a very small army, but when the battle started seven days later the Lord gave the victory to the Israelites and they killed a hundred thousand men of the Syrian army. The rest of the Syrians fled to a city called Aphek, where many more were killed when a great wall fell down on them.

Benhadad himself escaped and hid. Some of his followers said to him,

*Ahab fights the Syrians outside Samaria (**in distance**).*

405

"We have heard that the kings of Israel are merciful. Perhaps Ahab, king of Israel, will spare your life if we go to him humbly."

Benhadad gave them permission to go and they approached Ahab in great humility.

"Benhadad has sent us to beg that you will allow him to live," they said.

"But wasn't he killed in the battle?" asked Ahab.

"No, he still lives," was the answer.

"Go back to your king, and tell him to come here and speak to me himself," said Ahab.

When Benhadad came to Ahab, the king of Israel took him into his own chariot, and treated him very courteously. Benhadad promised to give Ahab some cities in return for his life, and Ahab accepted and let Benhadad return to Syria unmolested.

The Lord was angry at Ahab for letting his own greed, and his desire to rule over these other cities, come before the safety of his people. The Lord sent a prophet to speak to him.

"The Lord gave Benhadad into your hands because he should have been destroyed," said the prophet. "For this you will pay with your own life."

This prophecy was fulfilled some years later.

11

The story of the wicked Jezebel

HAB'S MOST IMPORTANT PALACE was in Samaria, but he had another palace in the city of Jezreel. In Jezreel there lived a man named Naboth, and Naboth had a vineyard that Ahab wanted very much to own.

"Sell me your vineyard," said Ahab to Naboth. "I will give you a better one in exchange, or if you prefer, I will pay you whatever it is worth in money."

Naboth did not wish to sell his vineyard, which had been his inheritance from his father. He did not want another vineyard, nor did he want money.

Ahab was very much disappointed. Like a spoiled child, he lay down on his bed and sulked. He would not even eat his meals. At length Jezebel, his wife, came to find out what was the matter with him.

"What is wrong?" she asked.

"I tried to buy the vineyard of Naboth, and he refused to sell it to me!" said Ahab.

"You are the king of Israel!" exclaimed Jezebel. "You do not have to tolerate a refusal to sell. But never mind. Get up, and enjoy your food. I will obtain the vineyard of Naboth for you, since you want it so!"

Jezebel's plan was an evil one, because it meant not only depriving a man of that which was rightfully his but also sending an innocent man to his death.

Jezebel wrote letters to the elders of the city of Jezreel, and signed them with Ahab's name, and placed his royal seal on them. In the letters she told the elders to find men who were willing to lie about Naboth, and pretend that they had heard him speak evil of God and of the king.

The elders of Jezreel did what she said, thinking they had received an order from their king. Everyone was wicked and sinful in this matter. Although the Commandments of the Lord said that no one should bear false witness against his neighbor, the elders found two men who were willing to swear that Naboth had spoken evil of God and of the king.

Naboth is killed
Another law was that any man who spoke evil of God must be put to death by stoning. Now the elders pretended that Naboth had been guilty of this sin and therefore should be stoned to death. He was taken out of the city, and stoned until he died. Savage dogs of the neighborhood came to the spot and licked up his blood. Word was sent to Jezebel that Naboth was dead.

Jezebel was pleased with the success of her plot and went to Ahab to tell him about it.

"The vineyard of Naboth is yours," she said. "Naboth is dead, and can no longer refuse to let you have it."

Ahab was delighted, and went to Naboth's vineyard to claim it as his own.

In all this time, Elijah the prophet, along with his assistant, Elisha, had been traveling throughout the land. Now the Lord commanded Elijah to go and meet Ahab at Jezreel and told Elijah what to say to the king.

Elijah obeyed, and when Ahab saw him he was vastly disturbed.

"So you have found me, my enemy," said Ahab.

"I have been sent to see you because you have given yourself up to a life of sin against the Lord," said Elijah.

Elijah then told Ahab the things that the Lord had commanded him to say.

"God will send trouble to you and to your family, until everyone in your family has been destroyed," said Elijah. "Your family will perish, just as the family of Jeroboam perished. You will die, and dogs will lap up your blood. As for your wife, Jezebel, dogs will devour her flesh by the wall of Jezreel, at the very spot where Naboth was so cruelly killed."

Not until years later was Elijah's prophecy about Jezebel fulfilled, but it was not long before Ahab died. He was killed in battle by the same King Benhadad whom he had freed after their earlier war.

At the same time that Ahab was king of the northern kingdom of Israel, a king named Jehoshaphat was ruling the southern kingdom of Judah. Ahab persuaded Jehoshaphat to help him fight Benhadad.

Ahab called together four hundred prophets and they told him he would be victorious over Benhadad; but these were false prophets, serving the heathen god Baal. Jehoshaphat was a good king, serving God, and he refused to believe anyone but a prophet of the Lord. So the two kings called such a prophet, a man named Micaiah.

"I see the soldiers of Israel scattered after the battle, like sheep without a shepherd," said Micaiah. He meant that Ahab would be killed in battle, and afterward the soldiers would be scattered because their leader was gone.

Ahab was so angry at Micaiah that he commanded the governor of the city to put the prophet in prison. Then he persuaded Jehoshaphat to go out to battle with him anyway. To protect himself, Ahab disguised himself in the armor of a common soldier. He did not wear the robes that marked him as a king.

But during the battle, a Syrian soldier shot an arrow in the direction of the Israelites, without aiming at any particular person or spot. The Lord guided the flight of that arrow and made it strike a small opening where two pieces of Ahab's armor breastplate came together. Ahab died of the wound that night, his army fled, and Jehoshaphat went back home to Judah.

The dead body of Ahab was carried to Samaria and buried there. As men were washing the blood from his chariot in a pool of water near the city, dogs came and licked up the blood, as Elijah had prophesied.

Ahaziah, Ahab's son, became the next king of Israel. He was a wicked man, like his father, but he reigned for only two years. Then he died and Jehoram, his brother, became king.

12

The story of Elijah and the fiery chariot

WHEN ELIJAH WAS A VERY OLD MAN, the Lord allowed him to know that it was time for him to be taken up into heaven. With Elisha, the man who was to be the greatest prophet of Israel after Elijah's death, he went to a place called Gilgal.

Elijah wanted to be alone when the Lord called him to heaven.

"I must go to Bethel, for the Lord has told me so," said Elijah to Elisha, "but I think you should stay here."

"No," said Elisha. "As surely as there is a God in heaven, I will not leave you as long as you live."

Together they went to Bethel. At Bethel there was a school where young men were taught the ways of the Lord by holy prophets. Some of the young men came out to speak to Elisha. They had seen a vision of Elijah's going to heaven.

"Do you know that the Lord is going to take your master from you today?" they asked Elisha.

"Yes, I know," said Elisha. "Say no more about it."

At Bethel, Elijah tried again to persuade Elisha to let him die alone.

"The Lord tells me to go to Jericho," Elijah said. "But you stay here, in Bethel."

"No," said Elisha. "As surely as there is a God in heaven, I will not leave you as long as you live."

They traveled on to Jericho. There also the young men in the schools taught by the prophets came out to speak to Elisha, having seen a vision.

"Do you know that the Lord is going to take your master from you today?" they asked Elisha.

"Yes, I know," said Elisha. "Say no more about it."

For the third time Elijah tried to make Elisha leave him.

"The Lord has told me that I must go to the River Jordan," said Elijah. "But I beg you, remain here in Jericho and let me go alone."

"No," said Elisha again. "As surely as there is a God in heaven, I will never leave you while you are alive."

Once again, the two journeyed on. This time, fifty young men from the schools of the prophets followed after them, a good distance back, so that they might see what would happen. When Elijah and Elisha stood beside the River Jordan, Elijah removed his cloak and struck the waters with it. The waters parted for him, and the two men walked across to the other side on dry ground.

When they reached the other side, Elijah spoke lovingly to his assistant, Elisha.

"What last thing can I do for you, before the Lord takes me away?" he said.

"Let my heart have more of God's spirit, as yours does, so that I may be worthy to serve as a prophet of the Lord," said Elisha.

"This is a very difficult thing you ask" said Elijah. "However, if you can see me when I am taken by the Lord, then you will be granted the request you have made. If you do not see me, then you will not be granted this request."

They walked on together, talking as old friends do, and suddenly there appeared a fiery chariot, drawn by fiery horses. Elijah was taken into the chariot, and it drove him swiftly up toward heaven and out of the sight of earth.

Elisha saw the chariot and its flight, and he cried out after Elijah,

"My father, my father!" This was the way people addressed a prophet in those days. "You were the chariot and the horsemen of Israel!"

By this Elisha meant that if the people of Israel had followed Elijah's leadership, they would have risen above all earthly trouble as Elijah had risen in the Lord's fiery chariot.

Elijah was gone, and Elisha picked up his mantle, or robe, where it had fallen from him. With the robe of Elijah, Elisha struck the waters of the Jordan and they parted for him as they had for Elijah. Then Elisha walked back to the side of the river where Jericho stood.

Elisha sees Elijah taken to heaven in a fiery chariot.

The fifty young men came to meet him. They saw that Elijah was no longer with him.

"Let us go and look for your master," they said. "It may be that the Lord has taken him to some mountain and left him there, or perhaps he is resting in a valley beyond the hills."

Elisha knew this was not so, and that Elijah would never return. He told the young men not to search, but they continued to plead until Elisha let them go. For three days they looked for Elijah, but of course they did not find him.

The men of Jericho invited Elisha to make his home there.

Elisha's first miracle

"Our city is a pleasant one," they said, "except that there is something wrong with the water. It is not good to drink and it is bad for the soil. Nothing will grow here."

Elisha then demonstrated that he was able to perform miracles as Elijah had done.

"Give me a new water bottle, and put some salt in it," he said.

They did so, and Elisha went to the spring from which the water of the city flowed. He threw the salt into the water, and spoke again.

"The Lord says that He has now made these waters sweet," said Elisha.

From that day on, the waters of Jericho were pure.

13

The story of Elisha's miracles

URING THE YEARS THAT Elisha was the great prophet of Israel, he astonished the people with his many miracles. Of course, it was actually God and not Elisha who performed the miracles. Sometimes Elisha prayed for a miracle and God granted his prayer; and sometimes God let Elisha know in advance that a miracle would occur.

The first of Elisha's miracles, after he purified the water of Jericho, was done for a poor widow who asked him to help her.

"My husband is dead," she told him. "He was a good man and spent his life in the service of the Lord, but he owed some money when he died. Now the man he owed it to is going to take my two sons and make them his slaves."

"Have you nothing of value?" Elisha asked.

"Nothing but a pot of oil," said the woman sadly.

"That is enough," said Elisha. "Go to all your neighbors and borrow as many empty vessels as they have. Take them to your house and shut the door. Then pour out the oil from the pot you have into the empty vessels that you will borrow. As soon as one is full, set it aside and fill the next."

The woman did as Elisha had told her, and as long as she poured there was oil to fill the borrowed vessels. When there were no more empty vessels, the oil stopped coming.

"Now sell the oil and pay your husband's debt," Elisha told her. "There will be some money left to buy food for yourself and your children."

The Woman of Shunem In Elisha's travels he passed through a city called Shunem. A rich woman who lived there invited him to her house.

"Rest a while, and have something to eat," she said.

She was so kind that Elisha visited her house every time he passed through Shunem. She even prepared a special room for him.

Once when Elisha was traveling with his servant, Gehazi, and stayed in Shunem, he asked the woman if he could do anything to help her.

"You are most kind, but I have everything I need," she answered.

Elisha still wished to reward the good woman.

"What can we do for her?" he asked Gehazi thoughtfully.

"She has no children," Gehazi said, "and her husband is old."

"That is it," said Elisha.

When Elisha promised her that the Lord would send her a son, she could scarcely believe him. She had been married for many years and had never had a child. The words of the prophet came true, however, and the woman of Shunem had a son. Elisha had asked the Lord to do this for her.

When the child was older, one day he was out in the field with his father

The widow's small jar of oil fills all the big jars.

during the reaping of the grain. Suddenly he became ill. He was carried home, where his mother held him on her lap to comfort him, but he did not get better and at noon he died.

The mother carried him to the little room she kept for Elisha, and laid him on the bed. Then she shut the door and went out. She did not tell her husband that their son was dead, but she asked that an ass be saddled so she could ride to Elisha.

"Why do you want to see the prophet today?" her husband asked curiously.

"I must go," said the woman simply.

As swiftly as possible, the woman rode to Elisha at Mount Carmel. When Elisha learned that her boy was dead, he sent Gehazi to the house.

"Take my staff and lay it across the face of the child," Elisha commanded his servant.

Gehazi left immediately, but the woman refused to go unless Elisha himself went along with her, and he finally agreed.

Gehazi, meanwhile, had done as Elisha told him, but the child did not recover. When Elisha reached the house he found the boy lying on the bed, dead.

Then Elisha prayed to the Lord, with the door of the room closed. For a long time Elisha prayed, and the flesh of the boy became warm again. Then Elisha left the room for a time, and walked up and down in the house, still praying to the Lord. When he returned to the room where the boy was lying, the child sneezed seven times, and opened his eyes, and came back to life.

Elisha called the boy's mother, and she fell on her knees in gratitude to the Lord and to the Lord's servant, Elisha.

All of Elisha's miracles were done to help people. Once when a group of young men, studying to be prophets, had eaten some soup that by mistake contained a poisonous vine, Elisha made the soup safe so that they would not die. Once, during a great shortage of food, he made twenty loaves of bread and a few ears of grain feed a hundred men. And once when a poor workman dropped an axe-head in the River Jordan, Elisha made the iron axe-head float on the water so that the workman could recover it. Iron was very precious in those times and a poor man could not afford to lose a valuable tool.

14

The story of the siege of Jerusalem

OR THE FOURTH TIME, BENHADAD, the king of Syria, decided to make war on Israel. He sent his soldiers to capture Jehoram, who was then king of Israel. But Elisha was given the power to see that the Syrians were coming, and he warned Jehoram.

Several times this happened. Each time the Syrians approached, no matter how secretly Benhadad gave his instructions, the king of Israel was always warned in time to escape.

"Someone in my army, or among my servants, must be on the side of the king of Israel," said Benhadad.

"No, master," answered his servants. "It is the prophet, Elisha. He knows what you plan even though you discuss it only in a locked room."

"In that case, capture Elisha," said the king of Syria. "Then he cannot tell Jehoram when we are coming."

Benhadad's scouts learned that Elisha was in the city of Dothan, and during the night the king of Syria sent many soldiers there. In the morning, Elisha's servant saw the forces of Syria encircling the city.

"What shall we do, master?" the servant asked Elisha.

"Do not be afraid," said Elisha.

When the soldiers of Benhadad reached the part of the city where Elisha lived, Elisha asked the Lord to make them blind. The Lord did so, and the soldiers could not see Elisha to capture him.

Elisha went out and spoke to them, as they groped about.

"Come with me," he said. "I will take you to the man you are looking for."

With that he led them to the city of Samaria, Jehoram's capital. When they reached the king, Elisha prayed that the men's blindness might be lifted, and it was. They suddenly saw where Elisha had led them.

During the siege of Samaria an ass's head sold for eighty silver dollars.

Jehoram asked if he should have them all killed.

"No," said Elisha. "Give them some food to eat and let them go back to their own land in peace." So Jehoram let the soldiers go back to Benhadad.

Not long after this, Benhadad gathered his army together and attacked Samaria. The Syrian soldiers surrounded the city and laid siege to it. They set up a blockade so that nothing could be taken into the city itself, and soon the people had used up their entire supply of food. Their hunger was dreadful.

For some reason, Jehoram blamed the hunger of the people on the prophet of the Lord, instead of on his own sins and on the sins of the people. Jehoram gave orders to have Elisha put to death.

The king calls on Elisha — Elisha was told by the Lord that a messenger was coming to kill him, and he told his servants to close and lock the door of the house. However, it was the king himself who came to Elisha's door, along with one of his officers.

"The Lord has said that there will be plenty of food in the city tomorrow," said Elisha.

Elisha kneels as Elijah is carried to heaven

Naaman's wife is advised to send him to Elisha

"That is impossible," said the officer of the king.

"Because you refuse to believe the words of the Lord, you will not be allowed to eat any of the food that the Lord is going to send," said Elisha, "though you will see it."

Outside of the city gate, four Israelites were seated. They were all lepers.

"What are we going to do?" said one of them. "If we sit here, we will starve. If we go inside the city, we will starve there too. We might as well go out to the camp of the Syrians. They may kill us, but we are sure to die anyway, so what does it matter?"

They went out to the camp of the Syrians, and to their astonishment they found it deserted.

The lepers did not know it, but during the night the Lord had made the Syrians think they heard the noise of a great army coming toward them with many chariots and horses. It had sounded like such a huge army that the Syrians fled for their lives, leaving their gold and silver, their clothing, and most important of all, great supplies of food.

The lepers ate until they were no longer hungry, and they took some gold and silver and clothing for themselves. But one of them said,

"We are not doing the right thing. We should go and tell the king of Israel that there is food here."

They went to the gate of the city and told what they had seen. Jehoram was doubtful, for he distrusted the Syrians.

The Syrians flee from the imaginary attack when they hear noises in the night.

"They have probably gone a little way out of the camp to lie in wait for us," he said.

So Jehoram sent out only a few men, as scouts, but they went as far as the Jordan River and saw no sign of the Syrian army. They did see clothing and other articles dropped by the fleeing army along the way.

When the scouts reported what they had seen, the people of the starving city rushed to the camp for food.

The king sent along the officer who had doubted Elisha's prophecy of the day before, and the rest of Elisha's words came true. The officer did see the food that the Lord had sent, but he did not live to eat any of it. He was standing at the entrance to the camp, and the crowd was so great that a mob crowded upon him and he was trodden under foot and killed.

Elisha's prophecy to Hazael

Elisha went to the city of Damascus, where Benhadad, the king of Syria, lived. Benhadad was sick, and when he learned that Elisha was in his city he sent one of his officers to ask the prophet if he would live or die. The officer's name was Hazael.

"My master the king is sick," said Hezael. "He has sent me with these presents for you, and to ask you if he will recover." Hazael had taken with him forty camels laden with all the good things of Damascus as a gift for the prophet of the Lord.

"He is not too sick to recover," said Elisha. "His illness will not kill him, but the Lord tells me that he will die anyway."

Then Elisha began to weep.

"Why are you weeping?" Hazael asked.

"I am sorrowful when I think of the evil things you are going to do," said Elisha. "You will burn the cities of the Israelites, and kill their young men in battle, and murder their women and little children."

"Do you think that I am such a vile creature as all that?" exclaimed Hazael.

"The Lord had told me that you will be king of Syria," said Elisha, "and your armies will do this."

Hazael returned to the king and reported that Elisha had said that the king would recover. The next day, however, Hazael took a thick cloth, and wet it, and held it over the king's face as he lay helpless in bed. The king was suffocated and died, and Hazael made himself king.

15

The story of Naaman

THE CAPTAIN OF BENHADAD'S ARMY was a man named Naaman. He was a brilliant soldier and a brave man, and he had won many battles for Benhadad. Unfortunately, Naaman had the disease called leprosy.

In Naaman's house was an Israelite girl who waited on his wife. She had been brought out of the land of Israel as a captive during one of the wars between Benhadad and the king of Israel, but she remembered well the prophet, Elisha.

"If your husband could see the prophet in Samaria, his leprosy might be healed," the girl told Naaman's wife.

The king was told what the maid had said. At once he told Naaman to go to Samaria, and he gave Naaman a letter to Jehoram, the king of Israel. However, Benhadad's letter failed to mention Elisha. It merely said that he had sent Naaman to Jehoram to be cured of leprosy.

"How can I cure him of leprosy?" Jehoram cried. "I have no divine powers!"

Jehoram thought that Benhadad was trying to find an excuse for another war with Israel, by giving Jehoram an impossible task to perform.

When Elisha heard of Jehoram's distress, he sent a message saying, "Send the man to me, and he will soon be convinced that there is a prophet of the true God in Israel."

Naaman drove in his chariot to the house of Elisha and stood at the door. Elisha sent a messenger to tell Naaman what he must do.

"Go to the River Jordan," said the message. "Wash seven times in the river, and your leprosy will be gone from you."

Naaman was angry because Elisha himself had not come out to pray to the Lord in Naaman's presence.

"If it is just a matter of washing in a river, there are plenty of good rivers in Syria!" he said angrily to his servants. Naaman's servants, however, were wiser than Naaman.

"Master, if the prophet had told you to do something extremely difficult, wouldn't you have done it?" they asked. "Surely it would be wise to do the thing he has told you."

At length Naaman agreed and went to the River Jordan, where he washed himself seven times as Elisha had told him to do. After he had finished, all trace of his leprosy had disappeared.

Naaman returned to Elisha's house and begged the prophet to accept a gift.

"No, I will not accept a gift from you," said Elisha, though Naaman urged him repeatedly to take something.

Finally Naaman asked permission to take some earth home with him

Naaman washes in the Jordan and is cured of leprosy.

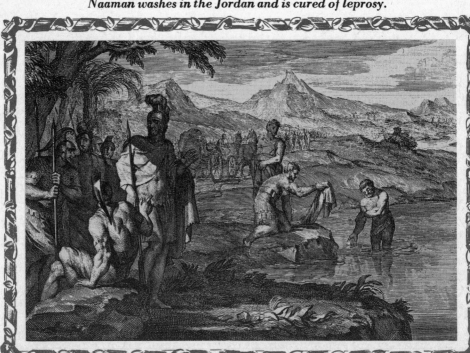

from Israel to Syria. He had determined to build an altar to the Lord.

"However, my master, the king of Syria, will want me to go with him to the idol's house when he worships," said Naaman to Elisha. "Will the Lord forgive me if I do so, and bow down when my master bows down, as long as I do not worship the idol in my heart?"

Elisha told him that the Lord would understand and forgive.

The sin of Gehazi

Naaman then left for his own home. He had been gone only a short time when Gehazi, Elisha's servant, determined to do a very wicked thing.

"My master did not accept any presents from that man," said Gehazi to himself, "but there is no reason I should not get something."

Gehazi followed Naaman, and when the Syrian saw him running after him he stopped his chariot.

"Is everything all right?" Naaman asked.

"Oh, yes, everything is all right," answered Gehazi. "However, after you left two young men who are students of other prophets came to my master, and he sent me to ask if you would be willing to give them a talent of silver and two changes of clothing."

"Certainly!" said Naaman. "Take them two talents of silver. They are most welcome to it!"

A talent of silver was a large quantity, weighing more than 50 pounds, and each talent was bound up in a bag. The entire gift was so heavy that Naaman sent two of his servants to carry it for Gehazi. When they reached Elisha's house, Gehazi hid the gifts so that Elisha would not know what he had done.

When Elisha asked his servant where he had been, Gehazi attempted to lie; but he could not deceive Elisha, for the Lord had already let Elisha know the truth.

As punishment for this sin, Elisha told Gehazi, the leprosy of which Naaman had been cured would now appear on Gehazi instead. In a moment, Gehazi was afflicted with leprosy and his skin became as white as snow.

16

The story of Jehu and Jezebel

HE WICKED JEZEBEL, WHO HAD BEEN QUEEN while Ahab was alive, was still living in the city of Jezreel, and Jehoram, her son, who was king of Israel, was staying there with her for a time. Elisha knew that soon there must be another king over Israel, because the Lord had told him so, and one day Elisha called a young prophet to him.

"Take some oil, and go to the city of Ramoth-gilead," said Elisha. "When you reach there, look for a captain named Jehu in the army of Israel. Take Jehu alone into a room and close the door. Then pour the oil from your bottle on his head and tell him that the Lord has anointed him to be king over Israel. Immediately after you have done this, get away from that place quickly, and return here."

The young man went to Ramoth-gilead, and there he found Jehu sitting with a group of other army captains. He told Jehu that there was a message for him, and Jehu went with him into the house. The young prophet then poured the oil on Jehu's head.

"The Lord has anointed you to be king over Israel. After you are made king, you are to put to death everyone who is left in the family of Ahab. This is the punishment for all the prophets of the Lord that Jezebel caused to be killed, and for Ahab's wickedness."

When Jehu rejoined the other captains, they wanted to know what the young man had said to him.

"He told me that the Lord anointed me to be king over Israel," said Jehu.

The captains immediately started to celebrate, and they blew trumpets loudly in honor of the occasion.

"Jehu is king!" they cried.

"I will go to Jehoram myself and tell him that you have made me king," said Jehu.

Jehu rode to Jezreel in his chariot, and the watchman on the tower gate told Jehoram of his coming. Jehoram sent out a man to ask whether Jehu came on a peaceful or warlike mission. Jehu would not answer the man, but told him merely to follow behind his chariot. Another man soon came out, and Jehu would not answer him either, but made him follow behind his chariot with the first man.

When his men did not return to report, Jehoram himself went out to meet Jehu.

"Do you come in peace, Jehu?" Jehoram asked.

"How can there be any real peace as long as your mother continues to sin all the time?" Jehu asked. "Jezebel is the most evil woman who ever lived!"

Jehoram knew then that Jehu had come to fight him, and he turned his royal chariot to flee. Jehu drew his bow and shot an arrow after Jehoram. It struck Jehoram in the heart and he fell down dead in his chariot. Jehu then ordered his captain to throw Jehoram's dead body on the ground, and it fell to earth in the very vineyard that Ahab had taken from Naboth.

As Jehu entered the city, Jezebel, Jehoram's mother, heard of his coming. She decked herself in her finest ornaments and painted her face. As Jehu came through the gates and passed her house she spoke to him from her window.

There were two or three officers in the house with her, and Jehu addressed them, rather than Jezebel.

"If you are on my side, then throw the woman to the ground," he said.

The officers did as Jehu said. They threw the wicked Jezebel out of the window, and when she fell her blood splashed on the wall of the house. Jehu's horses trod her under their feet.

The dogs that ran wild in the city devoured Jezebel's body, just as Elijah had predicted many years before that they would. When Jehu returned to the spot to bury her body, it was gone.

Jehu then fulfilled the rest of the prophecy spoken by Elijah many years before. He killed all that were left in the family of Ahab.

Jezebel is thrown out of the window to Jehu's army: A Doré engraving.

But Jehu was a wicked king and did not live according to the laws of God. He reigned for twenty-eight years, and when he died his son Jehoahaz became king.

17

The story of Amos and the fall of Israel

 EHOAHAZ, THE NEW KING OF ISRAEL after Jehoram was killed, was wicked, as his father had been. The Lord was angry and let Hazael, the new king of Syria, attack the Israelites and defeat them badly. Then Hazael did just as the prophet Elisha had predicted. He burned the cities, he killed the young men, and he murdered the women and children.

Finally Jehoahaz was stripped of all his armies. Hazael allowed him to keep only fifty horsemen, ten chariots, and ten thousand foot soldiers. Hazael did this so that Jehoahaz would never be strong enough to rebel against him. After seventeen years, Johoahaz died and his son Jehoash became king.

By now Elisha was very old and was about to die. As he lay sick on his bed, King Jehoash came to see him. The king wept.

Elisha told the king to take his bow and arrow and shoot an arrow out of the window to the east.

"That," said Elisha, "is a sign that you will defeat the Syrian armies of Hazael in battle." The Israelites, all this time, had been subject to Syria.

Elisha then told King Jehoash to take an arrow and strike the ground. The king did so, but he struck the ground only three times.

"You should have struck five or six times," said Elisha. "If you had, you would have been able to defeat the Syrians five or six times, and they would have been completely destroyed. But you struck only three times, and that means you will be able to win only three victories over them."

Elisha died and was buried, and after his death Jehoash fought against the Syrians, as Elisha had said he would, but he won only three victories.

Jehoash was king for sixteen years. Then he died and his son Jeroboam became king. This was the second king of Israel named Jeroboam.

Under the rule of King Jeroboam, the people of Israel were permitted to take two cities from the Syrians, because the Lord saw how they suffered under Syrian domination and had pity on them; but the people were not grateful to the Lord for His help, and instead of worshiping Him they continued to worship their golden idols.

Amos goes

to Israel

God sent the prophet Amos from his own land of Judah to speak to them.

"You are the people that the Lord once chose for His own," said Amos, "and still you do not serve the Lord Who has saved you so many times from your enemies. You have disobeyed His commandments and you have served false gods, worshiping idols. You have been cruel to the poor. You deceive and cheat one another. You scorn people who are righteous and overlook the sins of the wicked."

Amos was only telling the people what God had told him to say, but they did not pay attention to him.

"You have known how the Lord punishes you for your sins by sending disease and famine on the land," Amos continued. "Now he is going to send a much greater punishment on you. An enemy will come and conquer you and make you captives in a foreign country."

Amos told the people that if they would repent and obey the laws of God, the Lord would forgive them.

"But if you do not repent, you will suffer as you have never suffered before!" he declared.

At the temple of the idol in Bethel, there was a priest named Amaziah. He spoke to Amos.

"If you must prophesy in such a fashion," said Amaziah, "then go to the land of Judah and prophesy to the people there. This is the land of Jeroboam, and here the people worship idols."

"I was not born as a prophet," Amos said. "I was not even the son of a prophet. I was a simple herdsman, and a gatherer of wild figs. As I was driving my flock in the field one day, the Lord told men to go and prophesy to the people of Israel. Now the Lord has told me how I must answer you. You tell me not to prophesy in Israel, but the Lord has told me to do so. For this, the Lord says that you shall be punished. Your wife will leave you, your sons and daughters will be killed, and you will die in a heathen land."

Another prophet of the times, Hosea, also spoke to the people of Israel and told them of the great punishment the Lord would send on those who did not repent of their sins.

King Jeroboam heard the words of both prophets, and the people of Israel heard them also, but none of them would listen.

After ruling forty-one years, Jeroboam died. His son Zachariah became king, but after six months a man named Shallum murdered him, and made himself king, but only for one month. Then Menahem killed Shallum and became king. He reigned for ten years, and throughout those ten years he was an evil and wicked ruler.

During the reign of Menahem the king of Assyria attacked Israel and

The people of Jerusalem are carried as captives to Babylon.

Menahem paid the king of Assyria, whose name was Pul, a tribute of a thousand talents of silver. Menahem did not have that much money himself, but he made all the rich men of the kingdom contribute. Pul was satisfied and returned to Assyria.

When Menahem died his son Pekahiah was made king of Israel. Pekahiah angered the Lord by worshiping idols. He was king for only two years, and then he was murdered by a man named Pekah, who was the son of Pekahiah's captain. Pekah became king, and he too was wicked. He tried to capture Jerusalem, where the king of Judah lived, but he could not.

Then the prophecy of Amos began to be fulfilled. The king of Assyria attacked Pekah and carried away many of his people as captives.

Pekah had been king for twenty years when a man named Hoshea rebelled against him. Hoshea murdered Pekah and made himself king in Pekah's place. But Hoshea displeased the Lord during his nine years as king, because he sinned constantly. One more time the king of Assyria attacked, and Hoshea was frightened enough to promise that he would pay tribute. But Hoshea failed to send the tribute money and the king of Assyria came and put Hoshea in prison.

The king of Assyria then went through the land of Israel and took the people away as captives to the land of Assyria. He gave them cities to live in, but he would not allow them to return to Israel.

The end of the kingdom of Israel In this way the kingdom of Israel came to an end. It had survived for more than two hundred and nine years from the time that the ten northern tribes had chosen Jeroboam instead of Rehoboam as their king.

Nineteen kings had ruled over Israel since then, and all of the kings had been evil. Some were more wicked than others, but none had followed the laws of the Lord. The king of Assyria sent many of his own people to live in the cities of the Israelites, but the people of the ten tribes never returned.

No one knows what became of them, and history refers to them as the "Ten Lost Tribes of Israel."

18

The story of the early years of Judah

URING THE two hundred and nine years that the northern kingdom (the kingdom of Israel) lasted, the kingdom of Judah had also been having its troubles and its successes—its sins, and its punishments.

When Solomon died, the ten northern tribes chose Jeroboam as their king and Jeroboam set up a separate kingdom. Solomon's son Rehoboam was left to reign as king over the tribes of Judah and Benjamin. His capital was Jerusalem, the city of David, and his land was called the Kingdom of Judah.

The priests and Levites who lived with the northern tribes, when they learned they would not be allowed to worship God in Jeroboam's land, returned to the kingdom of Judah and acknowledged Rehoboam as their king. They were good people and made the kingdom of Judah larger and stronger when they joined it.

For three years Rehoboam obeyed the laws of God. Then, as his kingdom grew stronger and richer, Rehoboam grew bolder and less obedient to the Lord. At length Rehoboam felt that his power was great enough so that he need have no fear of losing his kingdom, and he began to sin as wickedly as the people of Israel were sinning under Jeroboam.

The people of Judah commenced to worship idols, and they built tall shrines for their false gods. They set idols on hilltops and on towers in their cities. At length they had returned to almost all the heathen practices that had caused the Lord to drive out the original people of Canaan.

Rehoboam built fortified cities throughout the kingdom of Judah. He made his land so strong that he felt no fear of an invader and thought he was powerful enough to resist any attack even without God's help.

Idolatry of Rehoboam, first king of Judah.

Rehoboam stationed his sons as commanders in different parts of Judah. Rehoboam had eighteen wives who were princesses and sixty of lower station, and in all he was the father of twenty-eight sons and sixty daughters. His favorite wife was Maachah, the daughter of David's son, Absalom, and Rehoboam chose her son, Abijah, to be the crown prince and to succeed him as king.

The attack of Shishak During the fifth year of Rehoboam's reign, a king of Egypt named Shishak marched on the kingdom of Judah with a great army. In the army there were twelve hundred war chariots, sixty thousand horsemen, and countless thousands of foot soldiers. As they advanced they captured the fortified cities that Rehoboam had thought so strong, and finally they threatened Jerusalem itself.

There the princes of Judah were gathered with Rehoboam, and they were all very frightened.

At this time a prophet of the Lord came to them. His name was Shem-

432

aiah. Once before he had helped Rehoboam. He had kept Rehoboam from sending the army of Judah to battle against the army of Israel under Jeroboam.

Shemaiah spoke to the king and princes of Judah.

"The Lord has said that because you have abandoned Him, He has abandoned you and will not save you from the king of Egypt," he said.

At that Rehoboam and all his men were greatly humbled and admitted that they had sinned. They bowed down to the Lord.

"God is right to punish us," they said. "We have done wrong, and we deserve His punishment."

When the Lord saw that they were truly repentant, He appeared again to Shemaiah. Shemaiah was told that Judah would not be destroyed by Shishak, king of Egypt. Instead, the people of Judah would become subjects of Shishak for a time, and perhaps they would learn how much better it was to serve the Lord; if so, they would be free again.

Shishak then took all the treasures of Solomon from the Temple at Jerusalem. He took even the golden shields that Solomon had ordered made, and Rehoboam substituted bronze shields for them.

Rehoboam died when he was fifty-eight years old, after reigning as king of Judah for seventeen years. After his death, his son Abijah became king.

Jeroboam was still reigning in Israel, where he had been king for seventeen years. Jeroboam gathered a great army of eight hundred thousand men and marched on Jerusalem, and Abijah made ready for battle. He had only four hundred thousand men, but he relied on the help of the Lord to make up for the difference in numbers.

Jeroboam persuades the Israelites

Before the battle began, Abijah went to a hilltop and spoke so that the men of Jeroboam, his enemy, could hear him.

"Listen to me," he said in loud, firm tones. "Surely you know that the Lord gave David and his descendants the right to rule over Israel. Surely you don't think you are able to withstand the power of the Lord. I see that you have brought your golden calves that you worship as gods. We have brought with us the power of the Lord."

While Abijah was speaking, Jeroboam led some of his forces behind the troops of Judah and attacked them from ambush.

The men of Judah prayed to the Lord for help, and the priests blew loudly on their trumpets. As the sound of the priests' trumpets filled the air, the army of Judah gave a great shout and the Lord made Jeroboam's men run wildly to escape. Abijah's army followed them, and in all they killed five hundred thousand of Jeroboam's best soldiers.

After the army of Jeroboam was thoroughly defeated, the men of Judah captured several cities from Israel. Jeroboam never again built up sufficient strength of arms and men to attack the kingdom of Judah, and just a few years after that disastrous battle Jeroboam died.

Abijah died when he had been king of Judah for only three years. His son Asa, a very good man, became ruler of the kingdom of Judah.

The priests blow on their trumpets as King Abijah waits on the hill.

19

The story of Asa and the Ethiopians

OR TEN YEARS AFTER ASA became king of Judah, the land was at peace. Asa destroyed the idols and images that the people had worshiped under the rules of Rehoboam and Abijah, and he restored the altar in the Temple of the Lord in Jerusalem.

Asa wanted to make certain that the land of Judah would be safe from enemy attack.

"Let us build more strong cities in the land," he said. "We will build barred walls, with sturdy gates, to surround our cities, and no one will be able to capture them."

The people did as Asa said, and for a long time there was peace and great prosperity in the country. But when Asa had been king for ten years, a vast army of Ethiopians marched toward Jerusalem. There were a million men and three hundred chariots in the attacking army.

Asa's army consisted of only five hundred and eighty thousand, but the army of Judah went out to meet the army of Ethiopia, which was led by a man named Zerah. Asa prayed to the Lord and asked Him to go with the Judeans, for Asa knew that no army, whatever its size, was strong enough to fight against the power of the Lord.

The Lord helped the people of Judah, and soon the Ethiopians were turned back. Asa's army pursued the fleeing men and killed them all. After gathering their booty from the battle, the victorious Judeans returned to Jerusalem.

At about that time, a prophet named Azariah spoke to Asa.

"You have lived according to the law of the Lord, and He has helped you," said Azariah. "As long as you serve the Lord, He will be with you;

but if you forget to serve the Lord, He will no longer give you His help. Do what is right in the eyes of the Lord and you will always be well rewarded."

The prophet's words encouraged Asa and his people. They made a great sacrifice to the Lord, consisting of a large number of the cattle they had captured from the Ethiopians. There were seven hundred cattle and seven thousand sheep.

Asa had been king of Judah for thirty-five years when Baasha, king of Israel, assembled an army to make war against him.

The defeat of Baasha This time Asa neglected to seek help from the Lord, and instead called upon the king of Syria to help him. "I am sending you treasures of silver and gold," he said in a message to the Syrian king. "Your father and my father were friends, just as you and I are friends. Please accept this gift, and in return help me to turn away the attack of Baasha."

The king of Syria did as Asa asked him to do. He sent armies to attack many different parts of Baasha's land. When Baasha learned that his cities were being captured by Syrians, he was forced to stop his advance toward Jerusalem and return to his own land to defend his cities.

Although Asa had been able to defeat the armies of Baasha because the king of Syria had drawn them away from Jerusalem, the Lord was displeased with Asa and sent a prophet to tell him that he had done wrongly.

"Why did you call upon the king of Syria for help, instead of the Lord, your God?" the prophet asked him. "The Lord was able to help you when the Ethiopian army attacked you, was He not? He let you defeat them and drive them away even though their strength was nearly twice as great as yours. You have acted wrongly, and the Lord will punish you."

Asa was very angry when the prophet spoke to him. "Put this man in prison," he commanded. So the prophet was unfairly imprisoned for telling the truth as the Lord had made him see it.

A year or so later, Asa developed a very painful ailment in his feet. It hurt him constantly, but once again Asa did the wrong thing. He depended upon his physicians to heal the disease, instead of praying to the Lord for help, and his feet were not healed.

Asa died in the forty-first year of his reign as king of Judah. His son Jehoshaphat became king of Judah.

20

The story of Jehoshaphat and his sons

EHOSHAPHAT, WHO BECAME king of Judah after the death of his father Asa, lived according to the laws of God. He sent teachers throughout the land to instruct the people, so that they would know the Lord's law. The kings of Judah before him had led the people back to idol worship, but Jehoshaphat showed them the right way and the Lord was pleased with him.

The heathen nations surrounding Judah were afraid to make war against Jehoshaphat. Instead they sent him tribute so that he would not decide to go to war against them. Soon Jehoshaphat became very rich and powerful, and he built entire cities in which to store his riches.

After Jehoshaphat had been king for several years, he made a journey to the land of Israel and visited King Ahab in the city of Samaria, the capital of Israel. There he arranged a marriage between his son Jehoram and the daughter of Ahab, whose name was Athalia. (Both Ahab and Jehoshaphat had sons named Jehoram.)

It was during this visit that Ahab was killed in battle. This is told in the story of Ahab.

The Lord sent a prophet to rebuke Jehoshaphat for allying himself with the wicked Ahab, and Jehoshaphat never went to Samaria again. He stayed in Judah and traveled throughout his land to the tell the people that they must stop all idol-worship.

After several years of peace and prosperity in Judah, the Moabites, Ammonites and Edomites assembled armies and marched toward Jerusalem to attack Jehoshaphat.

All the soldiers of Ammon, Moab, and Edom lie dead, killed by the Lord.

Jehoshaphat knew that he did not have enough strength to turn back such a mass of soldiers, but he was not afraid. He sent a message to his people.

"There are enemies coming to attack us," he said. "We ourselves can do nothing, but the Lord can save us. Let everyone fast and pray to the Lord, and the Lord will take care of us, as He always has done when we prayed humbly to Him."

All the people gathered together and prayed, as Jehoshaphat had told them to do, and once again the Lord sent a prophet to Jehoshaphat.

"The Lord says that you have nothing to fear," said the prophet. "Tomorrow you will go out against these people, and they will be by the brook in the desert. You will not have to fight them. Just stay there, and watch. The Lord will do everything that needs to be done."

The next day, when the army of Judah reached the brook where their enemies had been encamped, they found them all dead. The Lord had made them start fighting each other, and they were completely wiped out.

Jehoshaphat remained a good king, living according to the law of God. He reigned for twenty-five years, and when he died his son Jehoram became king.

Jehoram was the eldest of Jehoshaphat's seven sons, and Jehoram was an evil man. He killed all his brothers, for fear one of them might try to overthrow him and become king.

Jehoram's wickedness did not stop with the murder of his brothers. He returned to the worship of idols. His wife Athalia, the daughter of Ahab, influenced her husband in his wicked ways.

Elijah the prophet was still living at that time, and he sent a message to Jehoram, warning of what the Lord had in store for him as punishment for his wickedness.

"The Lord will send trouble to you and to your people," said Elijah's message. "You will lose everything, and then you yourself will become ill with a dreadful illness, from which you will not recover."

The prophecy was fulfilled when the Philistines and Arabians attacked Jerusalem and took away all of Jehoram's riches, and all his family except his youngest son, Ahaziah. Shortly afterward Jehoram became ill, as Elijah had said he would, and two years later he died. In all, Jehoram was king for eight years, and after his death Ahaziah became king of Judah.

The mother of Ahaziah had taught him the ways of wickedness, for she was the daughter of Ahab and all of Ahab's family were wicked. After having been king for only one year, Ahaziah went to visit Jehoram, king of Israel. (This Jehoram was the son of Ahab.)

It was while Ahaziah was visiting Jehoram of Israel that Jehu was anointed king of Israel, while King Jehoram was still alive. The story of Jehu and Jezebel describes what happened at that time. Ahaziah went out

The boy king Joash is crowned in the Temple.

to fight against Jehu and was killed as he tried to flee in his chariot.

When Ahaziah's mother, Athalia, learned that her son was dead, she killed all except one of Ahaziah's sons—her own grandchildren—because she wanted to make herself queen. The youngest boy, whose name was Joash, was hidden by his nurse in the Temple, where the high priest took care of him.

Athalia succeeded in making herself queen, and for six years the boy, Joash, was hidden from her. At the end of that time, however, the high priest, Jehoiada, told the Levites that one of Ahaziah's sons had been saved and ought to be king. They discussed the matter in secret and decided that the high priest was right. Accordingly, they arranged the traditional ceremonies for crowning a king, and they set up a guard around the Temple to protect the boy in case Athalia should hear of what they were doing and attempt to murder her one remaining grandson.

Joash was only seven years old when he was anointed king of Judah at the Temple. When the crown was placed on his head, the people shouted and clapped their hands.

"God save the king!" they cried.

Athalia heard the noise of their celebration. She hastened to the Temple. When she saw the boy wearing the crown of the king, she was furious.

"This is rebellion, and treason!" she cried.

Jehoiada knew that the people would surely kill her, and he warned them that she must not be slain in the house of the Lord. They took her outside and killed her a short distance away from the Temple.

Throughout the lifetime of Jehoiada, Joash was a good king and obeyed the laws of God. However, he only did so because of Jehoiada's influence. His heart was not in it. When Jehoiada died, one hundred and thirty years old, Joash no longer cared whether the people worshiped God or returned to idolatry.

The son of Jehoiada, a man named Zechariah (but not the prophet named on page 496), warned Joash that only trouble could follow if the commandments of the Lord were not obeyed, but Joash was angered by the words of Zechariah. He gave orders to have Zechariah stoned to death. This was done, but as Zechariah was dying he warned Joash once again.

"The Lord sees everything. He sees what you have done and He will punish you for your sins," said Zechariah.

The prophecy of the dying Zechariah came true within the year. An army of Syrians entered Jerusalem and killed many people. They took the silver and gold of the city and sent it to their own king at Damascus. The

Lord had allowed a small army of Syrians to defeat the much larger army of Judah. Joash himself became very sick, and as he lay helpless in bed his servants killed him.

Amaziah, son of Joash, reigned over the kingdom of Judah for twenty-nine years. During this time the army of Judah defeated the Edomites and in turn was defeated by the army of Israel. The Israelites took a great part of the treasure that was in the king's palace at Jerusalem, and they carried away some of the people of Judah as captives and took them to their own city of Samaria.

The people of Jerusalem were angry at Amaziah after what had happened. They rebelled against them, and as he was trying to escape they caught him and killed him. His son Uzziah then became king.

Uzziah was then only sixteen years old. He lived according to the laws of God during the first part of his reign, but as time went on he became very rich and strong and with his strength came pride and a disobedient spirit.

In defiance of the laws of God, which said that only priests could burn incense in the Temple, Uzziah went to the altar and started to burn incense himself. The priests warned Uzziah that the Lord would punish him, but Uzziah became angry at them for rebuking him. As he stood beside the altar, the white spot of leprosy suddenly appeared on his forehead. The priests put him out of the Temple as quickly as possible, and the king was forced to go and live by himself. He was never cured and lived the rest of his life alone.

After Uzziah died, Jotham became king, and Jotham tried to please the Lord in everything he did. He went to war against the Ammonites, and the Lord let him win the victory over them. After the Ammonites were defeated they paid Jotham great tributes each year and he became very rich.

Although Jotham himself was good, the people of Judah were sinful. They worshiped idols and disobeyed the Commandments. God then sent one of His greatest prophets, Isaiah, to guide them.

21

The story of Isaiah, the prophet of God

WHILE JOTHAM WAS KING of Judah, the Lord sent his prophet Isaiah to warn the people of the danger in their sinful ways of life.

"Even an ox knows the master who gives him his food," said Isaiah to the people. "The ox shows more gratitude than you, the people of Judah! You do not remember the Lord's goodness to you. You do not recognize the fact that everything you have and everything you have ever had came to you from the Lord!"

The land was filled with idols of worthless wood, and the people worshiped these idols as gods. Isaiah tried to tell the people of the Lord's wrath.

"The Lord does not want you to offer up sacrifices to Him in the Temple and then go out to worship your idols," said Isaiah. "You disobey the Lord's commandments, yet you expect Him to answer your prayers as if you were righteous people. The Lord will not listen to the prayers of such hypocrites. If you stop being evil, and learn once more the laws of the Lord, and live by them, then the Lord will forgive you and send his blessings to you!"

Still the people would not listen. The priests and the princes were as wicked as the rest of the people and none of them would leave their evil ways, in spite of Isaiah's grim warnings.

Only Jotham, the king himself, was good—in all the company of priests and princes that ruled over the people. Jotham listened to the words of Isaiah, and he tried in all his acts to please the Lord, but Jotham could not influence the others for the right, any more than Isaiah could. Then Isaiah gave the people further warnings.

"The Lord will send enemies from distant lands," said Isaiah. "They will come with great armies and fierce warriors. Their weapons will be sharp and deadly, and no one will be able to save the people of Judah."

The prophet Isaiah: A detail from the famous Michelangelo mural in the Sistine Chapel in the Vatican. ("Esaias" is another spelling of the name, used by Jesus.)

A vision of Isaiah: An angel purges his lips with a burning coal.

Still the Judeans paid no attention, when Isaiah told them that they would be taken captive by their enemies and there would be none left in the land of Judah. Weeds and briars would overrun the land, and the cities would be empty. Even the great city of Jerusalem, and the Temple itself, would be destroyed.

"These are the words of the Lord," said Isaiah. "Why will no one listen?"

Isaiah also prophesied that after many years a great king named Cyrus would rebuild the city and the Temple.

But the people refused to listen to Isaiah's preaching. The Lord took away their good king, Jotham, and his evil son Ahaz became king.

The reign of Ahaz Ahaz was a wicked king and led his people in the worship of heathen idols. The Lord was angry and sent the kings of Syria and Israel to battle against Ahaz. Pekah was king of Israel at that time, and he joined with the king of Syria in besieging the city of Jerusalem. In a single day, Pekah's army killed a hundred and twenty thousand men of Judah. Many others were taken captive and carried away to Damascus in Syria, and the king of

Israel captured many women and children, whom he took to Samaria in Israel, where he lived.

The Lord was not yet ready to let the kingdom of Judah be wholly destroyed by its enemies. Isaiah was sent by the Lord to Ahaz, to encourage the king and to tell him that he could be saved from his enemies if he would pray and ask help from the Lord.

"But I cannot bargain with God," Ahaz objected.

Isaiah was able to persuade Ahaz, and for the time being the kingdom of Judah was safe from its enemies, but the kingdom and Ahaz suffered great losses.

Then the Edomites and Philistines attacked Ahaz, and the wicked king begged Tiglath-pilezer, king of Assyria, to help him fight them. He sent the Assyrian king silver and gold from the Temple, and treasures from his own palace. The two kings captured the city of Damascus from the Syrians, but Ahaz did not derive any benefit from it.

Ahaz even closed up the Temple in Jerusalem, after he had taken out or destroyed the sacred things inside it. The final offense against the Lord was Ahaz's last, for he died, after being king for sixteen years. Then at last the people of Judah had a good king for a time. Hezekiah, Ahaz's son, was made king and immediately started to correct the evils that his father had committed. When Hezekiah became king of Judah, he immediately set to work restoring the Temple. He called upon the

The reign of Hezekiah priests and Levites to clean it thoroughly so that worship might be held there. In sixteen days they had cleaned the entire Temple and had put back all the sacred vessels that Ahaz had taken out.

The next morning Hezekiah called together the leading citizens of the city, and they took an offering of seven bullocks, seven rams, seven lambs, and seven goats. Hezekiah told the priests to offer these up on the altar as a sacrifice for all the sins of the people.

While the offerings were burning on the altar, the songs of praise to the Lord and the sound of trumpets and cymbals could be heard for miles around.

Hezekiah then invited the people to bring any offerings they wished, and their response delighted him, for they gave seventy bullocks, a hundred rams, and two hundred lambs. The king rejoiced that the Lord had made the people willing to bring offerings to the Temple once again, and that they would worship God there, instead of worshiping heathen idols.

Hezekiah's
Passover

Back in the days of Moses, many, many years before, the Lord had commanded his people always to observe the feast of the Passover, but it had been many years since they had done this. Now Hezekiah invited all the people of Judah, and all the men of the ten tribes of Israel, to come and celebrate the Passover feast in Jerusalem.

Most of the people in Israel laughed at Hezekiah and his invitation, but some were willing to repent of their sins and traveled to Jerusalem. In Judah, all the people were willing to take part in the feast. By the time they had all assembled there was a huge throng of them.

The Passover was observed exactly as it had been that night, long before, when the Lord had sent the destroying angel to kill all the firstborn sons of Egyptian families but pass over the Israelite houses marked with the blood of a lamb on the door. Hezekiah provided great numbers of cattle and sheep for sacrifice, and the people gave more, and the feast was the greatest that had been seen in the land since the days of Solomon. After the feast was over, the people went out in all parts of the land and destroyed all the idols they found, and the altars of the idols, in both Israel and Judah.

Isaiah and
the king
of Assyria

Some time later, the king of Assyria went to war against Judah and captured some of its cities. Hezekiah built up stronger walls about the city of Jerusalem and told his soldiers not to fear the king of Assyria or his armies, because the Lord was on the side of the people of Judah. With the Lord to help them, they could defeat any attacker.

Still, Hezekiah was afraid of the king of Assyria. In spite of his boasts, he sent the king presents of gold and silver.

The king accepted the gifts and returned to his own land. Later he returned with his army and again made war against Judah.

He stopped along the way and sent messengers ahead to Jerusalem, warning the people that he was going to attack them. He sent them also a special message.

"Do not believe Hezekiah when he says that the Lord will keep me from conquering you," said the message. "I will defeat you by the strength of my army. However, you can save yourselves. Give me gold and silver as tribute, and agree to serve me. Then I will not hurt you."

Hezekiah was terribly distressed. He called upon Isaiah, the prophet, to pray for the people. After praying, Isaiah sent word back to Hezekiah:

"Do not be afraid of the king of Assyria. The Lord will send a great punishment upon him, and his army will turn and go back to his own land. There the Lord will see to it that the king himself is put to death."

Then Hezekiah would not give up his city to the king of Assyria.

The Assyrian king reminded Hezekiah of how other lands had been conquered by the Assyrian armies.

"Do you think that your God can do better?" the king asked.

Hezekiah then prayed fervently to the Lord. He begged the Lord to deliver his people from the Assyrian armies. He asked for a powerful sign that the one true God was not like the helpless idols of other lands.

The Lord sent His prophet, Isaiah, to tell Hezekiah that a sign would be given and that the Lord would turn back the attack of the Assyrians. That very night, the Lord sent His destroying angel to the camp of the Assyrians, and the angel killed a hundred and eighty-five thousand men. The king of Assyria went back to his own land in shame and humiliation, and while he was worshiping his heathen idol his two sons killed him.

Shortly after this defeat of the Assyrians, Hezekiah became ill and Isaiah the prophet went to speak with him.

"The Lord has sent word that you are to die," said Isaiah. "It is time for you to prepare for death."

Then Isaiah left Hezekiah, and the king turned his face to the wall and prayed. "Lord," he prayed, "I have tried to serve You with all my heart, and have tried to do the things that would be pleasing and acceptable to You."

The Lord then sent Isaiah back to the bedside of the dying king.

"The Lord has heard your prayer and has seen your tears," Isaiah said to the king. "The Lord has decided to make you well. Three days from now you will be able to go to the Temple, and the Lord will add fifteen more years to your life."

When Hezekiah was well, as the Lord said he would be, he became more wealthy and powerful than he had ever been before. But he did not remain humble and grateful to the Lord. He grew proud and arrogant, with all

Isaiah tells Hezekiah that God will give him fifteen more years of life.

his riches and power. Even the king of Babylon heard of Hezekiah's riches and sent messengers to Jerusalem. Hezekiah boasted of his wealth to the messengers of the king of Babylon, and showed them about his palaces, letting them see all of his wealth and treasures.

"Who were those men, and what did you show them?" asked Isaiah. When Hezekiah told him that they had seen everything, Isaiah prophesied grimly to the king.

"The Lord has said that the day is coming when all the riches in your house will be carried away to Babylon. Nothing will be left. Some of your own descendants will be captured and will become servants to the king of Babylon!"

Hezekiah merely said that anything the Lord did was good and right, and it was kind of the Lord to keep these things from happening during his—Hezekiah's—lifetime.

Hezekiah reigned over Judah for twenty-nine years. His son Manasseh, who then was only twelve years old, became king at his father's death.

449

22

The story of the wars of Judah

ANASSEH BECAME KING OF JUDAH when he was only twelve years old, but in those days a youth of twelve was more a man than a boy.

Unfortunately, Manasseh was very evil. Instead of worshiping the Lord, as his father had done, he worshiped the sun and the moon and the stars as gods. He built altars to these false gods and led the people of Judah into heathen worship once again.

The Lord tried to warn Manasseh and the people, by sending prophets to them, but the people did not want to hear.

Then the Lord let the Assyrian army attack the people of Judah, and the Assyrians captured Manasseh. He had been hiding among the bushes, but they found him and bound him with heavy chains. He was taken to Babylon, and while he was imprisoned there he repented of his sins and prayed with all his heart to the Lord for forgiveness. The Lord heard him and allowed him to return to Jerusalem. Then Manasseh realized that he had been wrong in worshiping idols, and he commanded that all the idols be removed and their altars destroyed. He repaired the altar of the Lord and offered sacrifices on it.

Manasseh was king over Judah longer than any other ruler. He reigned for fifty-five years, and when he died his son Ammon became king.

Ammon was an idolator and a wicked king. His reign lasted for only two years, and then some of his ministers entered into a conspiracy against him and killed him. Ammon's son, Josiah, who was just eight years old, became the next king.

Jezebel is killed by Jehu's chariot

The Lord's destroying angel kills all the Assyrians

More than two hundred years before the birth of Josiah, a prophet in Israel had told Jeroboam, first king of Israel, that one day a king of Judah would go to Israel and burn the bones of men on the heathen altar. This king was Josiah. When he became king the ten tribes who lived in the northern kingdom of Israel had been carried away, and the kingdom of Israel no longer existed, but still Josiah fulfilled the prophecy.

Josiah began to serve the Lord while he was still a boy. When he became king he set out to destroy the idols and the heathen altars throughout the land. He ordered his soldiers to tear them down wherever they might be. Josiah also set men at work to repair the Temple, for it had been neglected during the years before Josiah's reign.

While the workmen were repairing the Temple, a high priest found the book of the law of God, the book written by Moses when the Lord gave him the law. The book consisted of a great roll of parchment, or thin sheepskin, which was used for paper then, and instead of being printed it was all written by hand. Printing and bookbinding had not yet been invented.

The people had been instructed to listen while the laws were read aloud

Manasseh sins by offering sacrifices to an idol (the statue above the altar).

to them once every seven years, but this had been neglected by the wicked people of Judah for a long time. Even Josiah had never seen the laws, but now the high priest read the laws to him.

Josiah then learned what punishments the Lord had promised to send if the people failed to obey His laws, and Josiah knew that for many years the laws had been ignored.

"What is going to happen to us?" he wailed. "We have not done the things God has commanded us to do, and He will certainly punish us."

Then he asked a high priest to consult a prophetess named Huldah, to find out what the Lord would do to punish the people of Judah.

"The Lord will punish Jerusalem and its people, who have not obeyed His laws," said Huldah. "However, because King Josiah has prayed for his people, and has turned back again into the way of the Lord, the punishment will not come during his lifetime."

After Josiah had heard the words of the prophetess he gathered the priests, the Levites, and the people all together and read them the words of the law. They all then promised to obey the commandments of the Lord.

All the vessels that had been used in offering sacrifices to the heathen god Baal were destroyed, and the priests of Baal were sent away.

Josiah then went to Bethel, where Jeroboam had heard the prophecy concerning the altar.

When Josiah reached Bethel, he saw some sepulchers, or coffins, on a hillside near the altar of Baal. From the sepulchers he took some of the bones of dead men and burned them on the altar, just as the prophet had foretold to Jeroboam. From that time, the altar would be considered permanently defiled, or unclean, and unfit for any kind of religious sacrifices. (Dead men's bones were considered extremely unclean in Biblical times, and to touch anything with them would make that thing unclean also.) Even worshipers of idols would have nothing to do with an altar so defiled.

Sins of the people Since the death of Hezekiah, the people had failed to keep the feast of the Passover, which was one of the Lord's commands. Josiah now reëstablished this feast. The people obeyed his commands and attended the feast, but they were not sincere worshipers of the Lord. They still had faith in their idols.

Jeremiah, a great prophet of God, tried to tell them that the Lord would

Josiah defiles the heathen altars by burning on them the bones of men.

punish them if they did not cease their evil ways, but they paid no attention. He reminded them of all they had received from God, and of their deliverance from Egypt, but still they scorned his advice. They even wanted to kill Jeremiah, but the Lord saved him.

Death of Josiah The king of Egypt now entered the land of Judah with a large army, and Josiah assembled his forces to fight him. "I have not come to fight your people," said the king in a message to Josiah. "I am here to make war against the king of Assyria. Return with your armies to your own home."

Instead of going home, however, Josiah changed clothing with another man, so that no one would recognize him by his royal robes, and he went into battle. Soon an arrow of one of the Egyptian soldiers struck him, and he told his servants to take him out of the battle.

"I am badly wounded," he said.

The Judeans placed their injured king in a chariot and removed him from the battle, but he died very shortly.

453

After the death of Josiah, his son Jehoahaz became king of Judah. But Jehoahaz reigned for only three months; then the king of Egypt attacked Jerusalem and captured him. He put Jehoahaz in chains and carried him to Egypt, where he remained a prisoner until he died. Pharaoh (the Egyptian king) made Jehoiakim, the brother of Jehoahaz, king of Israel next, but he compelled Jehoiakim to pay a high tribute in money.

The land of Judah was greatly weakened at that time, and the king of Egypt had taken so much money there was not a great deal left. The land was so weak that when the king of Babylon attacked the army of Judah, Jehoiakim was unable to resist. Instead he promised to be a subject of Nebuchadnezzar, king of Babylon. So all the people of Judah became subjects of Nebuchadnezzar.

23

The story of the prophet Jeremiah

EHOIAKIM HAD BEEN KING for a little over three years when the Lord spoke to the prophet Jeremiah and told him to write down in a book the punishments in store for the Israelites. These punishments would come only if the people failed to repent of their sins, and to live righteously. There was still time for them to repent and be forgiven by the Lord.

Jeremiah then approached a man named Baruch, who was called a scribe (which meant he knew how to write). Very few people other than some priests could write in those days.

Baruch wrote down all the words Jeremiah spoke, exactly as he spoke them. It was a large book when it was finished, and it contained a complete list of the punishments the Lord promised to inflict on the people if they did not repent.

"Now take the book to the Temple and read it aloud to the people, so that everyone will know what the Lord has said," Jeremiah told Baruch. The scribe did this, and the princes in the king's palace sent for Baruch and asked him to read the book to them also. When Baruch had finished reading, and they had heard all the list of punishments the Lord had in store for them and their people, they were very frightened.

"How did it happen that you wrote such things?" they asked Baruch.

"Jeremiah said all these things," Baruch answered. "As he spoke, I simply wrote down what he said."

"We must go and tell the king about this," said the princes. "But you and Jeremiah had better go and hide. The king may be very angry and try to harm you both."

The princes told King Jehoiakim about the book, as they had said they would do, and he sent a servant to fetch it to him. The king was seated beside an open fire on his hearth, and the servant read it to him there. As soon as the servant had finished reading a few pages, the king took a knife and cut them off, and tossed them into the fire. He listened a while longer, and then burned up the next section as the servant finished reading it. He continued in this manner, listening a while, and then burning up the part he had heard, until the entire book was destroyed by the fire. Some of the princes begged him not to do it, but he paid no attention. He cared nothing about the great trouble that would be visited on the people; he was only angry at Jeremiah and Baruch for having written the book. He sent soldiers to imprison them, but the Lord did not allow the soldiers to find the two men.

It did no good for the king to destroy the book, because the Lord told Jeremiah to repeat what he had said before, and Baruch wrote it again on another roll of parchment paper. This time the Lord told Jeremiah more things to include in the book.

The people of Judah hated Jeremiah for telling them of their sins, as all guilty persons dislike to be told of their guilt.

"I have done no evil," said Jeremiah, "and yet the people all hate me."

The Lord then promised Jeremiah that when the enemies of Jerusalem came to capture the city they would not harm Jeremiah.

Jehoiakim died after he had reigned for eleven years, and his son Jehoiachin became king. He ruled for only three months in Jerusalem, however, because King Nebuchadnezzar of Babylon attacked the city once again. Jehoiachin promised to live in submission to Nebuchadnezzar, and once again the king of Babylon went into the Temple to remove treasures and golden vessels. As he had done the last time, he went to the king's palace and took the king's treasures also. He did not stop there, however, as he had before. He took the king, his mother, his wives, and all the princes of Judah, and made them captives in Babylon. He also captured all the builders and carpenters and strong soldiers in Jerusalem and took them to Babylon.

There were many of the people of Judah taken as captives to Babylon, but there were still some left in their own land. Jeremiah wrote a letter to those who had been taken to Babylon. He told them to try to live con-

Jeremiah dictates his prophecies to the scribe Baruch.

tentedly in that land, because the Lord had said they would be there for
seventy years as servants to the king of Babylon. Jeremiah told them that
they should build houses for themselves, and plant good gardens, and in

general live normal lives. If they repented of all their past sins, and prayed for forgiveness, the Lord would pardon them at the end of the seventy years and would let them return to their own land.

Nebuchadnezzar made Jehoiachin's brother, Zedekiah, king over the people left in the land of Judah; but Zedekiah was little more than a servant to Nebuchadnezzar. After a short time, when Nebuchadnezzar had returned to his own land, Zedekiah rebelled. Nebuchadnezzar then besieged Jerusalem with his great army of Chaldeans, and no one could get in or out of the city.

Jeremiah the prophet was shut up in Jerusalem with the rest of the people, and King Zedekiah sent word to him, asking that he pray to the Lord for the safety of the city.

Jeremiah had to tell Zedekiah what the Lord told him to say.

"I cannot tell you that the Lord will save your city," said Jeremiah. "The Lord has said that the Chaldeans will capture Jerusalem and set fire to it. Still, if the people will bear the Lord's punishment willingly, and will go out to King Nebuchadnezzar and become his servants, then they will not be put to death. Whoever will stop fighting, and go out willingly to surrender, will be spared. All who stay in the city will be killed either in battle, by famine, or by disease."

The Lord had said these things, and they would therefore come true.

"Why do we not have Jeremiah put to death?" said some of the princes. "He frightens the people with the dreadful things he says."

"Do with him anything you choose!" said Zedekiah.

With that, the princes seized Jeremiah and lowered him by ropes into a deep pit that had a soft, muddy bottom. The pit was in a strong prison, but this part had no floor and Jeremiah's feet sank deeply into the mire.

One of the king's officers was alarmed when he learned what the princes had done to Jeremiah, and he spoke to the king.

"Your majesty," he said, "these men have acted very wrongly in putting Jeremiah into that dungeon. He will starve to death there."

"Very well," said Zedekiah. "Take some men and remove Jeremiah from the pit, so that he will not die there."

The officer selected some men to go with him. He took several pieces of old clothing and rags, which they lowered to Jeremiah on long ropes.

"Make pads of these pieces of clothing and rags, and put them under

Jeremiah: Above, Rembrandt's picture of the prophet. Right, Jeremiah is lowered into the dungeon. Below, he is pulled out.

The destruction and burning of Jerusalem by the Chaldeans.

the ropes by which we will pull you up, so that the rope will not cut into your flesh," the officer told him.

Jeremiah did so, and the men pulled him up by means of the ropes, and released him from the pit. They did not set him free, however, but placed him in another part of the prison.

After Jeremiah had been removed from the pit, the king sent for him and they talked in the entrance to the Temple, so that no one would hear what was said.

"I have a question for you," said the king. "Give me an honest answer, please."

"If I answer you honestly," said Jeremiah, "will you promise me that you will not have me put to death, even if the answer does not please you?"

"I promise solemnly that I will not have you put to death," said the king, "nor will I turn you over to men who want to kill you."

Then Jeremiah spoke.

"I know what your question is, because the Lord has told me what to say," he declared. "If you will surrender to the king of Babylon, and agree

460

to serve him, then neither you nor any of your family will be put to death, and the city will not be burned."

"But I am afraid that if I surrender to the Chaldeans they will turn me over to the people of Judah, who now are against me," said the king.

"The Chaldeans will not give you to them," said Jeremiah. "Please obey the command of the Lord, so that you may be spared. If you refuse, your wives and children will be given over to the Chaldeans, you will not escape yourself, and the city will be burned."

King Zedekiah did not obey the command of the Lord and surrender to the king of Babylon. As a result, the Chaldeans besieged the city for eighteen months, until there was nothing left inside the city walls for the people to eat. One night Zedekiah fled from Jerusalem with his family and with as much of his army as he could gather together, but the Chaldeans caught him and took him to the king of Babylon. Nebuchadnezzar killed Zedekiah's two sons and put out Zedekiah's eyes. Then he bound the blinded king with chains and took him to Babylon, where he held him in prison until he died.

The city of Jerusalem was burned and the walls around it were broken down. Nebuchadnezzar took all the treasures that were still left in the city, and carried away the people who were still alive in Jerusalem, leaving just a few men to work in the fields and vineyards. Nebuchadnezzar made a man called Gedaliah governor over the few who were left.

24

The story of the end of Judah

EDEKIAH WAS THE LAST KING of Judah, and that kingdom was ended when Nebuchadnezzar took its people away into captivity in Babylon.

The kingdom had lasted in all for three hundred and forty-four years after the death of Solomon. During that time it had nineteen kings and one queen. Only five of these were good kings who served the Lord. Even the good kings were not enough to make the people live righteously, however, and though the Lord sent prophets to warn them of what would happen to them, the people did not listen. Finally, the Lord did as He had said He would do if they did not better their ways. He took the land of Canaan away from the people of Judah.

The Lord had promised Jeremiah that the Chaldeans would not illtreat him after the city of Jerusalem had been captured and burned. The promise was fulfilled immediately after the fall of the city, when the king of Babylon spoke to the captain of his army.

"Do not harm Jeremiah under any circumstances," the king ordered. "Release him from prison, where the men of Judah have left him, and let him go wherever he wishes."

The captain did as his king had commanded.

"If you wish to go to Babylon with me, you may come," the captain said to Jeremiah. "However, you need not come if you do not want to. You may stay here or go wherever you choose. Also, if you like, you may go and live with Gedaliah, who has been made governor."

The captain then gave Jeremiah money and food and let him go. Jeremiah decided to live with Gedaliah, because he wanted to remain with those of his people who were still in the land of Canaan.

The Jews mourn for their destroyed city of Jerusalem: Doré's engraving.

After the Chaldeans captured the people of Jerusalem, some who had escaped fled into the desert and some went into other countries around Judah. When news reached them that Nebuchadnezzar had left some of the people still in the land, they returned to Judah. They could not go back to Jerusalem, because that city had been destroyed, but they went to Mizpeh, where the governor appointed by Nebuchadnezzar lived. Gedaliah was a kind man, and a good governor. He welcomed the returning Judeans kindly.

"Do not be afraid to come back and live on your own land," he said. "If you plant crops, and harvest your grain, and give your allegiance to the king of Babylon, no one will harm you."

With this reassurance, the people came back and cultivated the land. Their crops were good, and they grew plenty of fruit and grain for themselves.

One day some men visited Gedaliah and told him of a plot against him.

"Do you know that the king of the Ammonites has sent one of the princes of Judah to kill you?" they asked. "His name is Ishmael."

One of the men then took Gedaliah aside.

"Let me go and kill this Ishmael," he begged. "No one will know."

Gedaliah did not believe these men, and to the one who had asked permission to kill Ishmael he spoke sharply.

"You most certainly must not kill Ishmael," he said. "I do not believe that anyone wants to kill me!"

Gedaliah was wrong; the men had spoken the truth. A short time later, Ishmael and ten other men visited Gedaliah's house, pretending that they had stopped only to ask for food before continuing their journey. In those days, a man always offered food to a traveler who stopped at his house, because there were no hotels or inns.

Gedaliah was generous and gave the travelers food, but after they had eaten his food they killed him, and Ishmael fled to the land of the Ammonites.

After Gedaliah's death, the people still living in Judah were afraid that the king of Babylon would come and punish them for the death of his governor. In their fear they approached Jeremiah and asked him to pray to the Lord for them.

"I will pray for you," said Jeremiah. "But whatever the Lord tells me I will tell you, even if I feel that you will not be pleased at the answer."

"We will do whatever the Lord commands," they said.

Jeremiah then prayed to the Lord, and after ten days the Lord answered him and told him what to say to the people.

"The Lord has told me what I shall say to you," said Jeremiah to the people. "The Lord says that if you stay in this land, He will take care of you. You do not need to be afraid of the king of Babylon, because the Lord will make him kind to you. But if you go to Egypt, for fear that there will be war and famine in Canaan, you will suffer and will never see your own land again."

The people did not believe Jeremiah.

"You are not telling us the truth!" they cried. "You want us to stay here so that the Chaldeans can come and kill us all, or make us captives in Babylon!"

So once again the people did not believe the words of the prophet that the Lord had sent; and all the people, taking Jeremiah with them, moved out of Canaan into the land of Egypt.

Then the prophecy of Isaiah, made more than a hundred years before that time, was fulfilled—the land of Judah was left lonely and deserted, with weeds and briars growing everywhere, and filled with empty houses where no one lived any more.

25

The story of the prophet Ezekiel

T THE TIME WHEN JEREMIAH was serving as prophet of the Lord in Jerusalem, another man was doing the same thing for the people who had been taken captive by Nebuchadnezzar and carried to Babylon.

This man was Ezekiel, and he had been taken as captive to Babylon at the same time that Nebuchadnezzar had captured King Jehoiakim, his mother, his wives, and the princes of Judah.

The Lord appeared to Ezekiel in a vision, when the prophet had been in Babylon for a little more than four years. In that vision the Lord commanded Ezekiel to make a map of Jerusalem on a flat, earthenware tile and place it inside an iron pan, to symbolize the walls about the city of Jerusalem. On the outside of the iron pan he was to make a model of the forts of attacking soldiers, to indicate that the city was going to be under siege.

Ezekiel was then told to lie down on the ground beside this map of Jerusalem and stay there for many days. During those days he was to eat only a small quantity of coarse bread and drink only a small amount of water.

This was meant to tell the captive Israelites in Babylon of the fate that was in store for Jerusalem, when it would be under siege and the people in the city would have very little to eat.

Then the Lord told Ezekiel to take a razor, such as was used by barbers, and shave off the hair of his head and beard.

He should then divide the hair into three equal parts, weighing each part on a scale to make certain the three were exactly equal.

In his vision, Ezekiel is transported by God's power: A Raphael painting.

Ezekiel was then told to go to the place where he had left the map of Jerusalem, and burn one part of his hair there, as the city was later burned. Another part of his hair he was to cut up into small pieces with his knife, to symbolize the people who would be killed in battle against the forces of Nebuchadnezzar. The third part of the hair he was to hold up in his hand, and let the wind scatter it in all directions, to symbolize the way that all those left of the people of Judah would be scattered.

A year later, Ezekiel had another vision. This time it seemed that a great force lifted him by a lock of his hair and carried him from Babylon to Jerusalem. There he was told to look toward the north. Ezekiel looked and saw an idol set up near the Lord's altar.

There was still a further example of the people's wickedness that the Lord showed Ezekiel in his vision. Ezekiel was taken to the outer wall of the Temple and told to dig a hole through which he could creep inside and see what was going on. Ezekiel in his vision did so. He saw the elders of Israel burning incense to pictures of unclean beasts and to idols worshiped by the sinning people of Israel.

The Lord told Ezekiel that the people believed the Lord could not see them, because they were behind closed doors and worshiped their heathen idols in secret.

Another group of people, which the Lord showed to Ezekiel in his vision, were worshiping the sun as it rose in the sky. The Lord told Ezekiel how angry He was at all these things.

When the vision was over, Ezekiel thought that he was lifted again by a great force and removed from Jerusalem, where he had seen all these awful things, and taken back to the place from which he had started, a place by the river Chebar in Babylon.

Afterward Ezekiel told the people of Judah who were captives in Babylon what he had seen, but they did not believe him. They preferred to believe their heathen idols' prophets. The idols' prophets had said that the people of Jerusalem would not suffer and that their city would not be captured by the king of Babylon.

Ezekiel was given many instructions by the Lord. He was told to act like a man who was trying to escape without being noticed, to represent the attempt of King Zedekiah to escape from Jerusalem. He was told to act like a man who was afraid as he ate and drank that someone would take

Ezekiel's vision: He sees a chariot drawn by four manlike, winged creatures.

his food away from him before he had satisfied his hunger. This was to represent the fear that would be suffered by the Judeans in Jerusalem when their enemies came to attack them. Those enemies would surely attack, the Lord told Ezekiel, and they would destroy the cities of Judah, leaving them lonely and desolate, and they would carry away the people as captives.

On the day that the king of Babylon opened his attack against the city of Jerusalem, the Lord told Ezekiel to write down the date so that the people would always remember it. Ezekiel was told by the Lord of the siege that was taking place many miles away—long before news of the battle had time to travel so far.

Ezekiel told the people what the Lord had let him see, and they questioned him further.

"If the Lord is going to punish us, and destroy us for our sins, what can we do to save ourselves?" they asked.

"There is just one thing you can do," said Ezekiel. "Repent of your sins and live according to the laws of God. You know the Lord does not take

469

Ezekiel's vision: He is told to speak to the bones and restore life to them.

pleasure in punishing the evil men of this world. The Lord wants to see
His people turn from their wickedness, so that He will not need to punish
them."

Many months later, one of the men who had escaped from Jerusalem
reached the place where Ezekiel and the other captives were staying.

"Jerusalem has been taken by the King of Babylon," said the man.

When the captives heard this they knew that everything Ezekiel had
told them was true. Their false prophets had said that Jerusalem would
not be taken, but Ezekiel, the prophet of the Lord, had said it would be.

Then the Lord made it clear to Ezekiel that although the people of
Israel had to be punished, they were not to be entirely destroyed. They
would be punished for a time; but some day, when they had truly repented,
the Lord would once again take them for His people.

The Lord showed Ezekiel another wonderful vision. The prophet told
the people later what he had seen.

"It seemed that I was carried to a valley filled with dead men's bones—
old and dry bones," said Ezekiel. "Then the Lord told me to speak to the

dry bones and tell them that it was the command of the Lord that flesh should come on them again, and the breath of life should return to their bodies, and they should live."

Then Ezekiel explained the meaning of that vision.

"The people of Israel are like those dry bones," he said. "They have lost all hope of happiness, or of seeing their own land again. But just as the Lord raised the dry bones and brought them back to life, He will raise up the people of Israel and take them back to the land of Canaan."

There was one further demonstration of the Lord's power. Ezekiel took two sticks and wrote on one the name "Judah" and on the other the name "Israel." As he held the sticks close together, they grew together in his hand and became a single stick.

"But what is the meaning of this wonder of the Lord?" the people asked.

"The Lord means that when the people of Israel return to the land of Canaan they will no longer be divided into two nations but will be all one people," said Ezekiel.

Jeremiah had prophesied that the Israelites would remain as captives in Babylon for seventy years, and then would return to Canaan. This happened as he said, but this return was not the one predicted by Ezekiel. After the Babylonian captivity was over, the people who returned to Canaan sinned again and the Lord was angry. Thereafter they were scattered throughout the world, as they are even today.

In one of his visions, Ezekiel saw the Temple rebuilt and measured it.

26

The story of Daniel and the dream

HEN KING NEBUCHADNEZZAR was in Jerusalem, he told his chief officer to look over the princes of the land and select some of the most promising youths to be taught the language and customs of the Chaldeans.

"Find young men who are strong and handsome, with no bodily defects," he instructed the officer. "I want only the most intelligent, because I intend to make them my personal servants and take them to the palace with me."

Among the youths selected were four named Daniel, Hananiah, Mishael, and Azariah. The chief officer gave them Chaldean names, by which they were to be known in the city of Babylon. Daniel was called Belteshazzar; Hananiah became Shadrach; Mishael's name was changed to Meshach; and Azariah was known as Abednego.

They were taken to Babylon and teachers were assigned to instruct them in the wisdom and language of the Chaldeans. During their period of training, the king sent meat and wine to them from his own table.

However, Daniel and the three other young men did not want to eat the food prepared for the king's table. The Chaldeans worshiped idols and offered sacrifices to them, afterward eating the meat of the sacrifice. They also drank wine that had been used as offerings to idols. Daniel did not want to offend the Lord by eating food that was unclean by the Lord's law.

"We should not eat the king's food," said Daniel to Shadrach, Meshach, and Abednego. "We should not drink his wine."

"No, we should not," the other young men agreed. "What can we do?"

"We will speak to the officer who is in charge of such things," said Daniel, and when the man came again to see that they had food to eat, Daniel spoke to him.

"We would like your permission not to eat the food the king sends," said Daniel.

Although the officer had grown very fond of Daniel, he did not dare to grant that request.

"If you don't eat," he said, "you will grow thin and pale, and the king will have me put to death for not giving you the food as he commanded."

"I have a suggestion," said Daniel. "Give us only vegetables to eat, and water to drink, for just ten days. If there is any sign that we become thin or pale at the end of that time, you may give us whatever food you wish, and we will eat it, so that you will not risk punishment."

This request seemed reasonable, and was granted. For ten days the four young men ate only vegetables, and drank only water, and at the end of that time they were the strongest and healthiest-looking men of all those who had eaten the food from the king's table.

The Lord helped them all to gain a great deal of knowledge and wisdom, and He taught Daniel to interpret dreams.

After they had studied for three years, the four young Israelites were taken to the palace of the king. Nebuchadnezzar found that these four were wiser and more learned than any of the other wise men in his kingdom. He was greatly pleased with them.

Nebuchadnezzar's forgotten dream

One night Nebuchadnezzar had a dream that troubled him so much he could not sleep afterward. "I must know what that dream meant!" he exclaimed, and he ordered his attendants to call all the wise men in Babylon to the palace.

They assembled and stood before him.

"I have had a dream and it worries me. I have called you so that you may interpret it for me," said the king.

"Tell us your dream, your majesty," said the wise men.

"I cannot," the king confessed. "Much as it troubled me, I cannot remember it now. It has gone from my mind. It is up to you wise men to tell me what the dream was that I have forgotten, and then interpret it for me."

"But no man can do that!" exclaimed the wise men. "Tell us the dream, and we can interpret. But we cannot tell you your dream, if you have even forgotten it yourself!"

Daniel interprets the dream of King Nebuchadnezzar.

The king was very angry and gave orders for all the wise men of Babylon to be put to death. This would include Daniel and his three friends, Shadrach, Meshach, and Abednego, for they were among the wise men of the land. They had not been called with the others, however, to go before the king, and the first they knew of the order was when the king's servant came to them with his orders to kill them.

"Why does the king suddenly wish to kill all his wise men?" asked Daniel. The officer told Daniel what had happened, and Daniel went immediately to the king's palace.

"Instead of having all your wise men killed because they could not tell you your dream, allow me a little time, your majesty, and I will come back and tell you all that you wish to know," said Daniel.

The king then stopped the order for the killing of the wise men, to allow Daniel some time.

Daniel left the king and returned to where his three friends were waiting. He explained the situation, and asked them all to pray to the Lord for help. Then he and the three others prayed, and the Lord answered their prayers. He let Daniel know the dream, and also its interpretation, and Daniel went back to Nebuchadnezzar.

"Can you tell me the dream I have forgotten, and give me its interpretation?" the king demanded.

"No wise man on earth could tell the king what he had dreamed and forgotten. Only God could do that," said Daniel. "God has told me of your dream, so that I might tell you, and so that you will know that He is the true God."

Then Daniel told Nebuchadnezzar the forgotten dream.

Nebuchadnezzar had dreamed that he saw a great statue, with a head of gold, arms of silver, and body of brass. The statue's legs were iron and his feet part iron and part clay.

The head of gold meant Nebuchadnezzar's kingdom, because that was the greatest and richest on earth. The other materials in the rest of the image symbolized new but weaker kingdoms that would arise after Nebuchadnezzar's death.

Next, in the dream, a great rock fell from the mountain and shattered the feet of the statue, so that the rest of it fell down and splintered into tiny fragments—pieces as fine as dust, and so small that the wind blew them away. After the statue had been broken in the dream, Daniel continued, the rock that had fallen on it grew larger and larger, until it filled all the earth. Daniel next explained what the falling rock meant, and its growing large enough to fill the entire earth.

"The rock is the kingdom of the Christ, for it will break into pieces all the other kingdoms in the world. This kingdom will never be broken, but will grow as the rock grew in your dream and will someday fill all the earth."

Then Nebuchadnezzar knew that the God of Daniel was the God of gods and the King of kings. Nebuchadnezzar gave Daniel great honors and made him chief of the wise men. To please Daniel, he also gave his three friends high positions.

27

The story of the prophets in the fiery furnace

 ING NEBUCHADNEZZAR BUILT a great statue of gold and set it up on a plain. He then sent for all the rulers of his kingdom —the priests, the judges, the princes, the governors, and the captains—and assembled them all in the field in front of the statue. Then one of the king's servants made an announcement to the crowd, calling out to them all in a loud voice.

"This is the command of your king, Nebuchadnezzar," he cried. "As soon as you hear the sound of the harp, the flute, the trumpet, and all kinds of other music, you must fall down and worship the golden statue that Nebuchadnezzar, the king, has set up. Anyone who refuses to bow down and worship will be cast into the fiery furnace."

Then the king ordered the musicians to play, and when the people heard the sound of music they all bowed down and worshiped the idol, as the king had commanded.

However, Shadrach, Meshach, and Abednego did not bow down to worship the idol; because God's commandment forbids the worship of idols.

Some of the Chaldeans went quickly to the king and complained about the three men. Nebuchadnezzar had Shadrach, Meshach and Abednego brought before him.

"Is it true that you did not bow down and worship, as I commanded everyone to do?" he asked them.

"It is true, your majesty," they answered calmly.

"I will give you another chance," said Nebuchadnezzar. "When you hear again the sound of music, bow down and worship the golden image which I have set up. If you do not, you will be cast into the furnace and your God cannot save you then!"

Shadrach, Meshach and Abednego stand unharmed in the fiery furnace.

Shadrach, Meshach, and Abednego answered the king without fear.

"If you decide to cast us into the fiery furnace, our God can certainly save us if He chooses to do so. If He were to let us burn, still we will not worship an idol."

Nebuchadnezzar was furious. He ordered his servants to make the furnace seven times as hot as it had been before. They built the fire to a roaring inferno, so that it seemed nothing could withstand its searing flames. Then Nebuchadnezzar ordered his soldiers to bind Shadrach, Meshach, and Abednego, fully clothed, and cast them into the furnace.

To cast the three men into the flames, the soldiers had to go close to the furnace, and the heat from it killed them all. Shadrach, Meshach and Abednego fell down, bound, into the midst of the fire. Soon, however, they stood up and walked unharmed in the fire, for the Lord did not allow it to burn them.

Nebuchadnezzar suddenly gasped with alarm.

"Quickly, tell me!" he said to the people standing next to him. "Did we put the three men in the fire?"

"Yes, your majesty," he was answered.

"But I can see four men walking about in the midst of the flames, un-harmed!" gasped Nebuchadnezzar. "The fourth man looks as if he is the Son of God!"

Then Nebuchadnezzar called to the men in the fire and told them to come out, quickly. Shadrach, Meshach, and Abednego came out, and all the people who were gathered there saw that there was not a hair of their heads burned by the fire—nor was their clothing scorched, nor was there any smell of fire about them.

After he had witnessed this great miracle, Nebuchadnezzar gave bless-ings in the name of the God of Shadrach, Meshach, and Abednego. He knew then that their God was the only true God.

"And I make here and now a law, and a decree," he said. "No one in this land shall speak evil of the God of Shadrach, Meshach, and Abednego. Anyone who does so will be destroyed, and his house torn down."

After that, the three young men were made greater and more important than ever in Babylon.

Nebuchadnezzar's madness Nebuchadnezzar continued to rule in Babylon for many years, and everything went well for him. He felt so sure of his strength and power that he forgot God. God was displeased with him, and punished him. However, before the punishment was sent to Nebuchadnezzar, the Lord let him know through a dream what was going to happen. In the dream, which Daniel interpreted for Nebuchadnezzar, the king was sym-bolized as a great tree that was cut down, and for seven years was only a stump in the ground. That meant that Nebuchadnezzar would be cut down from his power, as the tree was cut down, and that for seven years he would be without a home or a palace and would live like the beasts of the field. After the seven years had passed, Nebuchadnezzar would have learned that God was all-powerful.

For seven years, it was as Daniel had said. Nebuchadnezzar became in-sane and spent his days in the fields, like the beasts that grazed there. At the end of the seven years, his reason was restored to him and he re-covered his kingdom and his riches.

Never again did Nebuchadnezzar turn away from the true God, whose power he had seen so vividly demonstrated in his own life.

28

The story of the handwriting on the wall

AFTER THE DEATH OF NEBUCHADNEZZAR, Belshazzar became king of Babylon. Daniel still lived there and he was still the wisest man in the kingdom.

One day Belshazzar held a great feast and invited a thousand of the lords and nobles to come and enjoy it with him.

As they were starting the feast, Belshazzar ordered his servants to bring out the gold and silver cups that his father, Nebuchadnezzar, had taken from the Temple in Jerusalem. The golden cups were brought and the people at the feast drank wine from them. As they drank, they gave praise to their idols of gold and silver, brass, iron, wood, and stone.

The feast was elaborate, and the great dining room of the palace rang with merry talk and gay laughter. In the midst of all the merriment, everyone was shocked and frightened when a man's hand suddenly appeared out of the air and wrote four strange words on the wall, where everyone could see them. The words were: MENE, MENE, TEKEL, UPHARSIN.

King Belshazzar was terrified. No one could read the language in which the words were written.

"Bring the wise men of the kingdom here quickly," cried Belshazzar to his servants. "I must know what the handwriting on the wall is supposed to mean."

The wise men soon were standing before the king.

"Whoever reads this writing and tells me what it means shall have the greatest rewards the kingdom has to offer," said Belshazzar. "I will give him a chain of gold to hang about his neck, and he will hold the third-highest position in the land."

The wise men were anxious to please the king, but none of them could read the writing. The language was strange to them. This frightened the king even more, but the queen suddenly thought of Daniel.

"Daniel has been known for many years as a very wise man," she said. "He was made master of all the wise men in Babylon during the time of Nebuchadnezzar, your father. He has the power to interpret dreams and secret meanings that are clear to no one else."

The king sent for Daniel and told him of the great reward that would be his if he could read the words on the wall and explain what they meant.

"I will read the words for you and tell you what they mean," said Daniel. "However, I want no reward and no gifts."

Then Daniel reminded Belshazzar of all the things Nebuchadnezzar had done, because God had made him great and strong. But, Daniel continued, when Nebuchadnezzar had achieved immense power, he became proud and forgot that it was God who had given him everything. For this he was punished for seven years. When he became humble again, and knew that God was the only true power, his reason and his kingdom and his riches had been restored to him.

"You knew all this," Daniel told the king. "Still, you have not acted righteously, and you have sinned against the Lord. You have taken the cups that came from the Temple of God and have drunk wine from them. You have given praise to your idols but you have not praised the one true God. Therefore these words of warning are written on your wall. It says MENE, MENE, TEKEL, UPHARSIN, which means that the Lord has tried you as king, but you have not done as you should have done, so your kingdom is to be taken away from you and the Lord will give it to the Medes and Persians."

Belshazzar kept his word about the reward, in spite of the fact that the words on the wall had been interpreted in a manner that was most terrible for him. Daniel was given a robe of scarlet, and a chain of gold to wear about his neck, and the king decreed that Daniel should be the third most powerful man in the kingdom.

That night everything happened just as Daniel had told Belshazzar it would. Cyrus the Great, a Persian general, captured Babylon and Belshazzar was killed. The army of Medes and Persians conquered the kingdom, and Darius, a Mede, was made king.

מקל ובריסין
חדף בוא

Daniel (pointing, at right) interprets the meaning of the Handwriting on the Wall while King Belshazzar and his attendants look on: Gustave Doré's engraving. See also the color rendition of the scene by Rafaello Busoni, facing page 482.

29

The story of Daniel in the lions' den

ARIUS LIKED DANIEL and had great respect for his wisdom and his goodness. He made Daniel the chief over all of the priests and princes of the kingdom, so that Daniel was second only to King Darius himself. This made the princes very angry and jealous. They plotted among themselves to find something evil in Daniel to tell the king. But no matter how they tried, they could discover nothing evil in Daniel.

"Unless this man does something to displease Darius in the manner in which he serves his God, we will never be able to complain to the king about him," they said.

They finally thought of a sly and wicked scheme to trap Daniel, and they went to Darius to execute their plans.

"All the princes of your kingdom ask that you make a decree, your majesty, that for the next thirty days no one may pray to any god except you, the king," they said. "Anyone who disobeys this decree will be cast into a den of lions."

Darius, who did not suspect them of evil motives, made the law and signed it. Once the Medes and Persians made a law, it could never be changed.

Daniel heard about the new law, but nevertheless he continued to pray three times a day and to give thanks to God as he had always done. The evil princes found him praying so, as they had known they would. Quickly they went to the king and told him that Daniel had been praying to God, which was contrary to the law.

"He must be cast into the den of lions," they demanded.

Darius was sorry he had signed the law, because he did not want to

Belshazzar sees the handwriting on the wall

Daniel in the lions' den

punish Daniel. He tried to find ways to avoid it, but toward evening the princes came to him and reminded him again that no law of the Medes and Persians could be changed. Darius had no choice but to order that Daniel be cast into the lions' den.

First he spoke to Daniel.

"Your God will protect you from the lions, because you serve Him so faithfully," said Darius. Then he went home, and spent the night fasting. He neither ate nor slept, and early in the morning he hurried to the lions' den and called out to Daniel.

"Daniel, Daniel!" cried the king. "Is your God able to save you from the lions?"

Daniel's voice came from inside the den of lions, calm and fearless.

"Yes, your majesty," said Daniel. "My God sent an angel to keep the lions from hurting me, because I have not sinned against the Lord. Nor have I done any wrong to you, your majesty."

When Darius heard these words he was very happy. He ordered that Daniel be released immediately from the den of lions. Daniel was set free,

The king comes to the lion's den and finds Daniel unharmed.

483

and there was no mark or injury of any kind on his body, because the Lord had protected him.

The king then commanded that the princes who had devised the wicked plot against Daniel be cast into the den of lions themselves—along with their entire families. As soon as they were thrown in among the lions, the lions attacked and killed them all.

When this had been done, Darius decreed that everyone in the kingdom must fear and respect the God of Daniel, for He was the living God and the only God whose kingdom would never end and would never be destroyed.

Daniel continued to prosper all during the reign of Darius; and after the death of Darius, when Cyrus became king, Daniel retained his high position in the land.

The angel Gabriel appears
While Daniel was in Babylon he read the words of Jeremiah, the prophet of the Lord. Jeremiah had written that after the Jews had been held captive in Babylon for seventy years they would be freed and allowed to return to their own land.

At the end of those seventy years, Daniel prayed to the Lord, and fasted. He asked that the people be allowed to go back, according to Jeremiah's prophecy. He prayed also that the city of Jerusalem might be rebuilt.

Daniel asked forgiveness for all the sins of the people, not because they truly deserved to be forgiven but because the Lord was a merciful God.

As Daniel was praying, the angel Gabriel flew by swiftly and touched him lightly.

"Daniel, I have come to tell you about the things that are going to happen," said the angel. "The Lord has heard your prayer and has sent me to speak to you. Your people will go back to their own land, as you have asked, and Jerusalem will be rebuilt. Four hundred and eighty-three years from that time the Saviour will be born, but the Jews will put him to death. Then, once more, enemies will come and Jerusalem and the Temple will be destroyed."

This was the end of the angel Gabriel's message to Daniel, and Daniel wrote it down as a prophecy of the Lord.

30

The major and the minor prophets

ANY MEN WERE PROPHETS OF THE LORD, but not all of them wrote books of the Bible. Of the prophets who wrote down their prophecies, four are called *major prophets*. They are Isaiah, Jeremiah, Ezekiel, and Daniel, and there is a story about each of them in this volume. Twelve are called *minor prophets*. The stories of some of them are told in this volume. Here are the names of all of them:

HOSEA lived about eight hundred years before Jesus was born. He was a prophet for sixty years, during the reigns of four kings of Judah: Uzziah, Jotham, Ahaz, and Hezekiah. Hosea warned the people of Israel against worshiping idols, as they were then doing, and prophesied the destruction of the northern kingdom of Israel. This occurred only a few years after Hosea's death.

JOEL lived about a hundred years after Hosea. He was a prophet in the kingdom of Judah while Josiah was king there. Joel prophesied that the Chaldeans (from Babylon) would invade Judah; that Jerusalem would be destroyed by the Romans, many years afterward; and that the Christian Church would arise and would become great and powerful.

AMOS was a herdsman in the southern kingdom of Judah, but he was sent by the Lord to prophesy in the northern kingdom of Israel. This was during the time when Hosea was prophesying in Judah. There is a separate story about Amos, beginning on page 433, in this volume.

OBADIAH began to prophesy about six hundred years before Jesus was born. He was one of the few prophets who foretold good things to come. He said that the Jews would one day be given a wonderful land of their own, and he prophesied God's severe punishment of the Edomites (a peo-

The minor prophets: Upper row, left to right, *Hosea, Joel, Amos.* Lower row, left to right, *Obadiah, Jonah, Micah.*

ple of a land near the land of Canaan) because the Edomites had ill-treated the Jews.

JONAH lived about eight hundred and fifty years before Jesus was born; some scholars believe that he was the earliest of all the minor prophets. The story of Jonah can be found in this volume, on page 526.

MICAH was a prophet in Judah during the life of Hosea. Isaiah was also alive then and Micah confirmed some of Isaiah's prophecies about the future sufferings of the Jewish people. The book of Micah includes some verses that are often quoted, especially the eighth verse of the sixth chapter. This verse tells us very simply and beautifully that we can please God if we are just, and merciful, and humble before God.

NAHUM lived about seven hundred years before Jesus was born. He prophesied that the great city of Nineveh, the capital of the conquering emperors of Assyria, would be completely destroyed. Jonah had made this prediction also, but the people of Nineveh had repented and the Lord had

The minor prophets: Upper row, left to right, *Nahum, Habakkuk, Zephaniah.* Lower row, left to right, *Haggai, Zechariah, Malachi.*

spared them. The prophesy of Nahum came true, for the people of Nineveh later returned to their evil ways and God destroyed their city completely.

HABAKKUK lived about a hundred years after Nahum, some six hundred years before the time of Jesus. Habakkuk was one of the prophets who foretold the fall of Jerusalem to King Nebuchadnezzar and his Chaldean armies.

ZEPHANIAH lived about six hundred and fifty years before Jesus, while Josiah was king of Judah. He too prophesied the punishment of the Jews for their sins, and also the punishment of the Philistines, Moabites, Ammonites, and Ethiopians.

HAGGAI was born while the Jews were captives in Babylonia, about five hundred years before Jesus was born. Haggai encouraged the Jewish people to rebuild the Temple in Jerusalem, when Cyrus permitted them to do so, as told in the following stories.

ZECHARIAH lived at about the same time as Haggai, and many of his prophecies were made while Darius was the Persian king and ruler of the Jews. Like Haggai, Zechariah encouraged the rebuilding of the Temple. Zechariah also made prophecies concerning the coming of the Messiah, or Christ; one of his prophecies foretold the thirty pieces of silver for which Judas would betray Jesus.

MALACHI was the last of the prophets whose books are in the Old Testament; he lived about four hundred years before the birth of Jesus. Malachi prophesied the coming of the Messiah, or Christ. One of the famous prophecies of Malachi concerns the forerunner of Christ, whom Christians later recognized in John the Baptist: "Behold, I will send my messenger, and he will prepare the way before me."

After the time of Malachi, for four hundred years, there were no men known to have the inspired gift of prophesying the works of God. During that period, therefore, there are only historical records to tell what happened to the people who worshiped God.

31

The story of the rebuilding of the Temple

THE JEWS REMAINED CAPTIVES in Babylon for seventy years, the length of time the Lord had told Jeremiah they would be held. Now, after these seventy years, a king named Cyrus ruled Persia and Babylon. The Lord made Cyrus willing to release the Jews, so that they could go back to the land of Canaan.

Jeremiah's prediction was not the only one that came true at that time. The prophet Isaiah, nearly two hundred years earlier, had foretold that a great king by the name of Cyrus would come to power and would rebuild the city of Jerusalem.

Cyrus made a proclamation and sent it to all parts of his kingdom.

"The Lord has told me to rebuild His Temple in Jerusalem. Any of the Jews who are captives here and who wish to return to their own land may go back and rebuild the Temple of the Lord, and the people of this kingdom will help them by making them gifts of gold and silver and cattle and clothing to take with them."

Almost all of the Jewish priests and Levites, and thousands of the other Jewish people, wanted to leave Babylon. The people of Babylon did as their king had commanded them and gave the Jews a great many presents. Then King Cyrus took the sacred vessels out of his storehouses—the vessels that Nebuchadnezzar had removed from the Temple in Jerusalem—and he counted them to make sure they were all there before giving them back to the prince of Judah who was going to lead his people back to the land of Canaan.

This prince's name was Zerubbabel, a descendant of King David. In all, Cyrus returned to him 5,400 of the sacred gold and silver vessels.

With Zerubbabel went 42,360 Israelites and 7,337 of their servants. They had 736 horses, 245 mules, 435 camels, and 6,720 asses. It was a huge caravan that finally arrived in the land of Canaan and reached the spot where the city of Jerusalem had once stood.

The ruins of Jerusalem   There was nothing to be seen except ruins. Jerusalem was just as Nebuchadnezzar had left it many years before. The walls of the city, all its houses, and the Temple itself had been completely torn down and then set on fire.

The people immediately began to rebuild the altar of the Lord that had stood in the court of the Temple. They built it as quickly as possible, so that they would have a suitable spot at which to worship the Lord. When the altar was finished they made offerings to the Lord each morning and evening, as the people of Israel had done before their long captivity in Babylon.

Then it was time to start rebuilding the Temple itself. As Solomon had done, they hired men of Tyre to cut down cedars on Mount Lebanon and send the wood by sea to a port near Jerusalem.

Work began immediately on the building of the Temple, and when the first stones of its foundation were laid there was great rejoicing among the people. Priests and Levites played their trumpets and clashed their cymbals, and everyone sang songs of praise to the Lord.

However, there were still many very old men who had seen the beautiful Temple of Solomon that once stood on that spot, and they wept as they remembered how it had been destroyed. The sound of weeping joined with the glad cries of the younger people, and it could be heard for miles around.

The trouble with the Samaritans   When the king of Assyria, Sennacherib, had conquered the ten tribes of the northern kingdom of Israel, long before Jerusalem was destroyed, he had sent people from his own land to live in the cities of the Israelites. These people were called Samaritans, and their country, once called Israel, was now called Samaria. The Samaritans worshiped idols, but they pretended to worship the Lord.

The Samaritans heard that the people of the southern kingdom of Judah had returned and were rebuilding the Temple in Jerusalem. They approached Zerubbabel and the rulers of the Jews.

Cyrus gives back the treasures taken from the Temple: A Doré engraving.

"Let us help you in your work," they said. "We too are worshipers of the Lord, and we have offered up sacrifices to Him ever since the king of Assyria sent us here."

491

They were lying, however, and the Lord made Zerubbabel refuse their assistance.

"You have nothing to do with building the Lord's house," said Zerubbabel. "We will build it ourselves, as Cyrus, king of Persia and Babylon, told us to do."

This angered the Samaritans, and they did everything in their power to hinder the rebuilding of the Temple. They even hired men to speak against the Jews to the officers of Cyrus. During the lifetime of Cyrus, they continued to trouble the people of Israel, but they were not successful.

Trouble with Artaxerxes

King Cyrus died, and a man named Artaxerxes became king. The Samaritans thought that a new king might be easily influenced against the Jews. They wrote him a letter and told him many things that were untrue.

"We think you should know that the Jews who returned from Babylon are rebuilding the wicked city of Jerusalem," the letter said. "If they finish what they are doing, they will not pay tribute to you as they should; they will undoubtedly rebel against you. The people of Jerusalem were always rebellious and were a great trouble to kings of long ago."

Artaxerxes believed the Samaritans. He inquired about the past history of Jerusalem, and he could not have been told the true story because he believed that Jerusalem had been rebellious long before that time, when actually the Jews had only been trying to defend their land from conquerors. At any rate, he wrote a letter to the Samaritans, in which he expressed his appreciation of their concern for him.

"I have learned that what you said is true," he said, "and I now give you permission to go and forbid the people of Jerusalem to continue with their building until I tell them that they may do so."

The Samaritans hurried to Jerusalem to deliver the king's message. During the lifetime of Artaxerxes, no more building was done on the Temple.

However, the people built themselves houses in which to live.

Darius and the prophet Haggai

Darius became king after the death of Artaxerxes, but the Jews did not ask his permission to finish the Temple. They had become more interested in building houses. This angered the Lord, Who sent the prophet Haggai to them.

The prophet Haggai urges the people on as they rebuild the Temple.

"You say it is not yet time to build the Temple for the Lord," said Haggai. "But is it right for you to be living in beautiful houses of your own, while His house is still in ruins?"

493

The people could not answer this.

"You have not prospered, and you have not been happy, because the Lord has not blessed you," Haggai continued. "Go up into the mountains, and cut wood for the building of the Lord's house, and He will be pleased and will bless you again."

Soon the people were busily at work again on the construction of the Temple. When the Samaritans saw what they were doing, they spoke to Zerubbabel and Jeshua, the high priest.

"Who has told you to go on building the Temple?" they demanded.

"King Cyrus long ago commanded us to come back here and rebuild the Temple of the Lord," said Zerubbabel and Jeshua.

The Samaritans then wrote a letter to Darius, the new king of Persia and Babylon. Darius, when he had read this letter, told his ministers to search through the books in which royal decrees were written, to see if what the Israelites claimed was true. He found that Cyrus had issued such a decree during the first year of his reign.

Rebuilding the Temple: Putting on the finishing touches.

494

The architects of the Temple consult as it nears completion.

When Darius had read this decree, he sent word to the Samaritans to leave the men of Judah alone. He told them also to give part of his own tribute, which they paid to him, to the Jews instead; and the Samaritans were to keep the priests supplied with animals for burnt offerings and with wheat, wine, and salt.

"If anyone fails to obey this law that I have made," said Darius, "timber shall be taken from his own house to build a gallows, and he shall be hanged on it. Then what is left of the house shall be torn down, until it is only a heap of ruins."

After this decree the Samaritans were afraid to trouble the people of Judah and the Jews finished building their Temple. When it was finished they held a great ceremony of dedication and offered up a hundred bullocks, two hundred rams, four hundred lambs, and twelve goats, as sacrifices to the Lord.

The feast of the Passover was celebrated during the first month after the completion of the Temple.

32

The story of Ezra and Nehemiah

WHILE ARTAXERXES WAS KING of Babylon, there was a Jewish priest named Ezra who had remained there after the first group of Israelites left for Jerusalem. He was a very holy man and taught the laws of the Lord to his people.

Ezra asked Artaxerxes for permission to go to Jerusalem to teach the Lord's law to the Jews who were already there. Artaxerxes not only gave Ezra permission to go, he gave the holy man gifts of gold and silver to take with him, as offerings to God, and he said that any Jews in Persia could go with Ezra to Jerusalem.

Artaxerxes did even more. He decreed that wherever Ezra went, in any of the provinces of his kingdom, the treasurers should give Ezra anything he needed—gold, silver, wheat, wine, oil, or salt. Artaxerxes did not wish to bring the Lord's anger upon his kingdom.

Ezra was commanded to select judges in the land of Judah, and to let them judge the people who would not obey the laws of God. Anyone who did not obey the law would be punished with whatever punishment those judges thought he deserved. He might be put to death, or sent away to another land, or deprived of his riches, or sent to prison.

After receiving this decree from Artaxerxes, Ezra gave thanks to God for putting kind thoughts into the king's heart. He then called together those priests, Levites, and chief men of the Jews who had remained in Babylon after Cyrus had released them. He took them to the banks of the river Ahava and told them to fast there for three days, and to pray for the Lord to show them the right way to go on their journey. Ezra had assured the king that the Lord would guard those who obeyed him, and therefore Ezra was ashamed to ask the king for an escort of soldiers to guard the traveling caravan of Jews.

Artaxerxes (with hands upraised) gives the Jews permission to return home.

Finally the Jewish people started out, with all the treasure that Artaxerxes had given them. Their wives and their little children went with them, and all along the route the Lord protected them so that none of the

497

bandits through whose land they passed could do them harm. In about four months they arrived in Jerusalem, and there they rested for three days. After that they went to the Temple and gave the silver and gold and other treasures to the priests and Levites at the Temple.

Back in Babylon, a Jew named Nehemiah was cupbearer to King Artaxerxes. This means that he carried wine or water to the king whenever the king wanted something to drink. Nehemiah heard that the people in Jerusalem were poor and very unhappy. A traveler told him that the walls of Jerusalem had never been rebuilt and were still in ruins.

This made Nehemiah himself unhappy, and he asked the king if he might go and help the people of Jerusalem to build up the walls of the city.

"How long will the journey take?" the king asked, "and when will you return?"

Nehemiah told him how long he thought it would take; this may have been two or more years, because people traveled slowly in those times. Nevertheless, the king gave him permission to go.

"One more request, your majesty," said Nehemiah. "Will you give me letters to the governors of the provinces through which I must pass, telling them to help me, and another letter to the keeper of the king's forest near Jerusalem, so that he will give me wood to make beams for the walls, and for the gates of the city?"

The Lord made Artaxerxes willing to give Nehemiah these letters, and Nehemiah set out, accompanied by soldiers and horsemen to guard him along the way.

When Nehemiah reached the provinces near Judah, he gave the king's letters to the governors. The governors themselves were friendly, but there were two men serving the governors who hated the Jews. When they learned that Artaxerxes had sent a man to help the Jews, these men were very displeased. The two men were named Sanballat and Tobiah.

Nehemiah reached Jerusalem safely and went to look at the walls of the city, to see if they were as bad as he had heard. He found the walls in ruins, just as he had been told.

The next day he called together the people of the city and told them why he was there.

"Without walls to guard your city, you are in danger of attack from our enemies," he said. "The king has given me permission to help rebuild the walls, so let us start work immediately."

"Yes, let us build the walls now!" exclaimed the people. Everyone fell to work with a will. Even the priests and the Levites helped.

Sanballat was angry. He made fun of the efforts of the Jewish people.

"These Jews are too weak to build a good wall!" he said. "Any wall they build will be so fragile that a fox that stepped on it would knock it down!"

The Jews were not discouraged. They continued to work until they had built the wall to half the height it would eventually reach. At this point it completely encircled the city.

Sanballat found that he could not discourage the Jews by making fun of them, so he conspired with Tobiah and other enemies of the Jews. They decided to attack the Jews without warning.

The walls of Jerusalem are manned

But the Jews were told of what their enemies had planned, and Nehemiah set armed men behind the wall.

"Don't be afraid of these people," said Nehemiah. "The Lord will help you and we will win the victory. You are fighting for your wives, your children, and your homes!"

When the enemies of the Jews learned that the Jews were prepared to defend themselves, the attack was not made.

After that, only half of the men of Israel worked on the wall, while the other half stood guard with swords, spears, and bows. Nehemiah stationed a trumpeter to sound the alarm in case an attack should come unexpectedly.

Day and night the men worked, and the rebuilding of the wall progressed rapidly.

Unfortunately, there was trouble within the ranks of the Jewish people. There were some who were very poor and some who were very rich. The poor people complained bitterly.

"We have had to pay tribute to the king, and we have had to buy food for ourselves and our children," they said. "Now all our money is gone. We have borrowed from our richer countrymen and they have taken everything from us."

"Yes," said others. "They have even taken our children as slaves, and we have not the money to buy them back. We love our children as much as they love theirs, and we are Jews just as much as are the rich princes and rulers who have taken our children."

Nehemiah was angry when he heard how the rich had treated the poor among them.

"Give back the houses and cattle and money that you have taken from your poorer countrymen, so that they will have money enough to buy back their children," said Nehemiah.

The princes and rulers agreed to do as Nehemiah had said, and Nehemiah made them swear before the priests that they would keep their word.

Meanwhile, Sanballat and Tobiah were afraid to go into Jerusalem, because they heard that the men of Israel were still at work on the wall and that it extended entirely around the city. They still wanted

The plot against Nehemiah

to harm Nehemiah, and to get him out where they would not risk harm to themselves, they sent a messenger asking him to come out of the city and talk with them.

"I am doing important work, and I cannot stop to come out and talk with you," said Nehemiah. He knew they just wanted to do him harm. Four times they asked him, and four times he refused.

Sanballat then tried another method of approaching Nehemiah. He sent a servant with a letter.

"I have heard that the Jews in Jerusalem are going to rebel against the king of Persia, and that you, Nehemiah, intend to make yourself their king," said the letter. "That is why you are so intent upon building up the wall around the city. Before I write and tell the king of Persia about this plot of yours, you had better come out and talk with me."

Nehemiah sent back an answer immediately.

"You know that what you said is not true. You are only pretending to believe these things because you are evil," said Nehemiah's letter. Then Nehemiah prayed that the Lord would let them finish the wall.

When Sanballat and Tobiah realized that they could not persuade Nehemiah to come out of the city to meet them, they hired a man in Jerusalem to frighten him. The man's name was Shemaiah. He shut himself up in his house and pretended that the Lord had given him a message for Nehemiah. Nehemiah went to the man's house to talk with him.

"Let us go to the Temple and shut the doors," said Shemaiah. "Your enemies are coming tonight to kill you."

"I am doing work for the Lord," said Nehemiah. "Should one who is doing the Lord's work stop in the midst of it, and run away?" Nehemiah knew that the Lord had not spoken to Shemaiah, and that this was just another of Sanballat's and Tobiah's schemes to hinder work on the wall. Nehemiah again prayed that the Lord would allow them to finish that work.

After fifty-two days the wall was completed and the people held a ceremony of dedication. The priests, the Levites and the people all went up to the top of the wall, in two great companies. One company went one way and the other went in the opposite direction. As they walked around the city, on top of the wall, they played on trumpets and harps and sang praises to the Lord. When the two companies met, they came down from the top of the wall and marched to the Temple, where the priests offered sacrifices to the Lord.

Nehemiah then set rulers over the city.

"Let the gates be closed at night and not opened until the sun is high in the morning," he said. "And let the men of Jerusalem take turns serving as guards, to watch over our city and warn of the approach of any enemies."

The feast *of trumpets* When the people of Israel were wandering in the desert, in the time of Moses, the Lord had commanded that silver trumpets be made for the priests to sound at the start of a journey. Since then, the people had celebrated the feast of trumpets on the first day of the seventh month every year.

After the completion of the wall around the city, it was time for the feast of trumpets to be held. The people asked Ezra, the prophet, to read to them out of the book of God's laws. Ezra did so, and the people were frightened, for they knew they had disobeyed many of the laws that Ezra had read. The Levites told them that this was no time to tremble and weep. This was a glad feast, and they should be happy.

Ezra taught the people much of God's law that day and the next, and the people were willing to promise that they would obey the commandments of the Lord. They wrote down all their promises on a paper, and everyone signed it.

Some time later, Nehemiah went back to Persia, as he had promised to do, and stayed for some time. The Bible does not say how long he remained in Persia, but it does say that when he returned to Jerusalem after that time, he found that the people had sinned again, and failed to keep their written promise to the Lord.

33

The story of Esther

FTER THE TIME OF DARIUS, there was a king in Persia and Babylon named Ahasuerus.

Not all the Jews in captivity had chosen to return to Canaan with either Zerubbabel or Ezra. Many of them still lived in Persia.

In the third year of his reign, Ahasuerus gave a great feast for the officials of his court, in the garden of his palace. There were beautiful decorations all about the palace. The people at the feast drank out of vessels made of gold, and the occasion was one of great celebration.

At the same time, Vashti, the queen, gave a feast for the women of the palace.

On the seventh day of the king's feast, when he had drunk a great deal of wine and perhaps was intoxicated, Ahasuerus sent for his wife, the queen Vashti. He commanded her to come with her crown on her head, and without her veil, so that everyone might see how beautiful she was.

This was a very strange thing for a king of Persia to ask, because the women of that land, in that time, were never seen publicly without veils to cover their faces. They even lived in a separate part of the house and never appeared before men. It was considered immodest for a woman to let her face be seen by anyone but her husband.

When King Ahasuerus told Vashti to come before the crowd of princes and people of the land, so that they might see her face without its veil, she refused to obey her husband's command.

The king was wildly angry at this. He asked his wise men for advice.

"Queen Vashti has not obeyed the command of the king, her husband," said Ahasuerus. "What shall we do to punish her suitably?"

Vashti (standing, in center) refuses to obey the orders of King Ahasuerus: Doré's interpretation, which is mistaken because she never did appear before the men.

"Queen Vashti has done wrong," the wise men replied. "Now that she has publicly disobeyed her husband, all the women of Persia will think that they too can disobey. This act of Queen Vashti's is a very bad example to the other women of the kingdom."

"But what shall we do?" asked the king.

"Let us make her punishment severe enough so that the other women of Persia will not be tempted to disobey their husbands," said the wise men. "Let it be known that Vashti will never again come into the presence of the king, and let the king choose for himself another wife—one who will obey her husband as a wife should."

The king punishes Vashti

This advice pleased the king and his princes, and he did as his wise men had suggested. He wrote the decree the wise men had advised and made it a part of the law of the land. Now Vashti could never see him again.

Then the advisors made another suggestion.

"We think it would be a good idea if your majesty sent officers throughout the kingdom to gather all the beautiful young women together in the palace at Shushan," they said. "The one who pleases your majesty most, out of all the beautiful young women in Persia, can be made your queen instead of the disobedient Vashti."

"This is a very good suggestion," said the king, and he ordered his officers to go through the kingdom as the wise men had advised.

One of the officials at the palace of Ahasuerus was a Jew named Mordecai, and he had a beautiful young cousin named Esther (or, under her Jewish name, Hadassah). Esther's mother and father had died and Mordecai had taken the young girl into his own house and had brought her up as his daughter.

When the time came for all the beautiful young women of Persia to be assembled at the palace in Shushan, Esther was among them. The officer of the king who had charge of attending to the needs of the women was very kind to Esther, because her charm and beauty pleased him greatly, and he assigned her to the best part of the house where the women stayed. He also gave her seven maids to wait on her.

Just before Esther went to the palace, her cousin Mordecai gave her a word of advice.

"It is not wise to let it be known that you are a Jewess," said Mordecai.

"Very well," Esther agreed. "I will not mention it."

When King Ahasuerus saw Esther, he lost all interest in the other young

Esther is overcome as she reports to Ahasuerus the plot against his life.

women. Esther was so lovely that he fell in love with her on the spot. He
placed the crown on her head and made her his queen in-
The king stead of Vashti. He then held a great feast for her, called
chooses Esther's feast, and his attendants were all given presents in
Esther her honor.

Esther remained obedient to Mordecai, even though she
was queen, because she felt toward him as a daughter feels toward her own
father.

After Esther had been queen for a short time she had a chance to do the
king a service, and it was her cousin Mordecai who gave her the opportunity.

There were two officers of the king who were angry at him for something,
and they plotted together, planning to kill him. Mordecai was a watchman
at the king's gate and he overheard the talk about their
The plot plot. Promptly he went to see Esther.
against "Two men are plotting to kill the king," he said. "You
Ahasuerus must warn him."

Esther told the king and when he checked on the story
he found that the two officers were guilty. He had them both put to death
for their treachery. Mordecai's action in reporting the plot was written
down in the book of records, where important incidents in the history of the
kingdom were noted.

34

The story of Haman and Mordecai

HERE WAS AN OFFICIAL in the palace of King Ahasuerus named Haman, and the king had given him a very high position in the court. All of the other officials had to bow to Haman whenever he passed, because the king had told them they must. Mordecai, however, did not do as the others did. He would not bow down before Haman, because he did not feel bound to obey any law but God's.

"Why do you not obey the king's command?" the other officials asked Mordecai. They warned Mordecai that it was dangerous to ignore a royal order, but Mordecai would not listen to them.

Haman became very angry and determined to punish Mordecai. He had learned that Mordecai was a Jew, and in his anger he decided to punish all the Jews in Persia along with Mordecai. He plotted carefully and devised a scheme that would make it appear that the king himself wanted the Jews destroyed.

Haman went to Ahasuerus and spoke against the Jews.

"Your majesty, there are some people living in your kingdom who have laws of their own that are different from the laws of your people. They do not obey your laws, but only their own," Haman told the king. "It is dangerous for you to let them live. I would be glad to pay ten thousand talents into the king's treasury for the sake of getting rid of these dangerous people. I beg your majesty to issue a decree that they should all be destroyed."

Ahasuerus believed the words of Haman, his trusted servant, and he gave Haman the ring from his finger. This was the same thing as signing his name to any decree that Haman might write, because in those days a law was marked by sealing it with the king's special ring.

"I give you my ring," said Ahasuerus. "Write whatever you wish in the decree, and seal it with this ring. As for the ten thousand talents you offered, you need not pay anything at all—and you may do whatever you choose to these people."

Destruction of the Jews is decreed

Haman was wickedly pleased with the success of his plan. He called the scribes—or writers—together. "Write a decree," he commanded. "In it, say that on the thirteenth day of the last month of the year, every Jew in Persia is to be killed—men, women, and children. Anyone who sees a Jew should kill him, and whoever does so may keep for himself the Jew's house, cattle, and money."

The scribes wrote the decree as Haman had said, and Haman sealed it with the king's ring, which made it officially the law of the land. Copies were sent by messenger to the governors and rulers of every province. When the messengers had left, Haman and the king sat down to drink wine together.

When Mordecai learned of what Haman had done, he was filled with sorrow for the troubles of his people. He put on sackcloth, which was a sign of grief and mourning, and he walked through the streets uttering sad and bitter cries. He went before the king's gate, but he could not go through because no one dressed in sackcloth was allowed inside the gate.

In every province throughout the land, the Jews were unhappy. Many of them did as Mordecai had done; they dressed themselves in sackcloth to demonstrate their sorrow.

Esther learns of the decree

Queen Esther had not heard about the decree, but then one of her maids told her that Mordecai had been seen in the street wearing sackcloth and mourning. Esther sent new clothing to her cousin, but he refused to remove the sackcloth.

Still Esther did not know why Mordecai was so sad. She then sent an officer of the king to go and ask Mordecai what was the matter.

"Here," said Mordecai to the soldier. "Take a copy of this decree to the queen and she will understand why I am sad. Ask her also to plead with the king to save the Jews in Persia."

The officer reported to Esther what her cousin had said, and she sent another message to him.

"It is well known that if anyone goes to the king without having been called by him, that person will be put to death, unless the king chooses to hold out his golden scepter as a sign that the intrusion is forgiven," said Esther's message. "I have not been called to the king's presence for the past thirty days. How do I dare go and speak to him?"

Mordecai sent back a second message.

"Do not think that the enemies of our people will let you live just because you are the queen," said Mordecai's message. "If you will not save the Jewish people now, someone else will save them—but you and all your relatives will be destroyed. And who knows? Perhaps the Lord made you queen just so that you would be in a position to save the Jews at this very moment."

Esther then instructed Mordecai to get all the Jews in the city to fast and pray for three days. She said, "I will do the same, and then I will go in to see the king, without having been summoned by him. If he chooses to have me put to death for this, then I am willing to die."

Esther carefully planned her attempt to save her people. She dressed herself in her royal robes, and she went to the entrance of the inner part of the palace where the king could see her as he sat on his throne. The Lord made the king feel kindly toward her, and the king held out his golden scepter, which meant that she was forgiven for entering without being summoned. Esther moved closer to the king and touched the top of the scepter, which was a sign of respect for the king.

"What is it you wish, Queen Esther?" the king asked. "Whatever it is, your request will be granted."

"If the king pleases," said Esther humbly, "I would like both the king and his minister, Haman, to come and enjoy a banquet that I have prepared today."

"Go to Haman and tell him to make ready," said the king to a servant standing nearby. "We will go to the banquet that the queen has prepared for us."

Esther's first banquet   At the banquet, the king asked again what favor Esther wanted to ask of him, because he knew that she must have wanted something very badly to dare visit his inner court without an invitation. Again the king said that no matter what she requested, her wish would be granted.

At her banquet for the king and Haman, Esther accuses Haman.

"If the king and Haman would be gracious enough to attend another banquet tomorrow, which I will prepare between now and then, I will tell the king what it is I would like to ask at that time," was Esther's reply.

Haman was very proud because he had attended a banquet at the queen's house and had been invited to come again next day. He passed Mordecai at the king's gate, and once again Mordecai failed to bow to him. This made Haman extremely angry, but he said nothing.

When he reached his own house, he called together his friends and sent for his wife. He wanted to boast of the honor that had been done him, and of his important position in the court.

"The king has set me above all his other servants," he bragged. "And what is more, Queen Esther invited me to go with the king to a banquet she had prepared. Tomorrow I go to another banquet at her house—and I am the only man besides the king who is invited. All these honors are very wonderful, but I cannot be truly happy about them while I see the Jew, Mordecai, sitting at the king's gate."

"Here is a suggestion for you," said his friends. "Let a high gallows be built—higher than any gallows has ever been before—and ask the king in the morning for permission to hang Mordecai on that gal-

Haman builds a gallows

lows. After Mordecai is dead, you can go to the Queen's banquet and enjoy yourself without care."

Haman was pleased with that plan, and ordered the gallows built immediately.

That night King Ahasuerus could not sleep, and to divert himself he ordered that his servants bring him the book in which important events of the kingdom were recorded. The book was brought and read to him. It happened that his servants read him the story of how Mordecai had saved the king's life by telling about the plot of the two soldiers. Ahasuerus asked what reward had been given to Mordecai for this.

"No reward was given him, Your Majesty," his servants answered.

As they were speaking, Haman came into the court. He had come to ask the king's permission to have Mordecai hanged in the morning, but before he had a chance to say anything, the king spoke.

"Tell me, Haman," said Ahasuerus. "What do you suggest that I should do for a man whom I want very much to honor?"

Haman immediately jumped to the conclusion that the king referred to himself, and he proceeded to tell the king of the kind of honor that would appeal most to him.

"Let the man whom the king wishes to honor be dressed in the king's

At the king's command, Mordecai is led in triumph through the streets.

royal robes, let him ride the king's horse, and let the king's crown be set on the head of the man the king wishes to honor. Then let one of the noble princes lead the horse on which the man is riding through the streets of the city, and call out that this is the king's favor to a man he wishes to honor."

"Very good!" said the king. "Now, take the robes, and my horse, and my crown, and go to Mordecai, the Jew. Let it be exactly as you have said. You may lead the horse through the town and call out that this is the king's favor to a man he wishes to honor."

Mordecai is honored

Haman did not dare disobey the king, but he was humiliated and angry that he was forced to show such honor and respect to a man he hated. After Mordecai had ridden through the town on the king's horse, dressed in the royal robes, and wearing the king's crown, he returned humbly to his seat outside the gate. Haman hurried home as quickly as possible, hiding his face in shame. He told his wife and friends of the embarrassment he had suffered, and as he was speaking a messenger came to take him to the banquet that Esther had prepared.

Haman is hanged on the high gallows he built for Mordecai.

This time when the king asked her what request she had to make of him, Esther answered him fully.

Esther's second banquet

"If the king is pleased with me, and wishes to grant my request, then let him save the lives of all the Jews, and my life as well. Evil things have been said about the Jews—things that are untrue—and an order has been issued that I and all of my people are to be killed."

King Ahasuerus was astonished, for he knew nothing about the decree that Haman had issued and sealed with the royal seal.

"Who has dared to do such a thing?" he demanded.

"This man, Haman," said Esther. "He is our enemy."

Haman was terrified, and the king was so angry that he left the room. Haman fell on his knees before Esther and begged for his life. When the king came back into the room, that was the position in which he found Haman. A soldier of the king spoke at that point.

"Outside of Haman's house is a gallows seventy-five feet high that Haman built to hang Mordecai," said the soldier.

The high hanging of Haman

The king ordered that Haman himself be hanged on the gallows he had built for Mordecai's execution, and when Haman had been hanged, the king was able to forget his anger.

Although Haman was dead, the decree that he had sent to all parts of the land was still in force, because once a decree became a law of the Medes and Persians, it could not be changed. Even the king himself could not change it, but he told Esther and Mordecai that they might issue another decree to save the Jews, and seal it with his royal seal, so that this too would become a law.

Mordecai quickly assembled the king's scribes and gave them a new decree to write. This decree said that all Jews had permission to gather themselves together on the thirteenth day of the last month of the year—the day on which their slaughter had been scheduled by Haman—and defend themselves against anyone who tried to harm them. They were given permission to kill any attackers with swords.

When the news of the second decree became known, there was great rejoicing among all the Jews. Messengers were sent to ride as fast as possible to all parts of the land, so that all people would hear

The feast of Purim

of the decree in time. Then the Jews armed themselves, and fought for their lives, and won the victory. Then for two days, on the fourteenth and fifteenth days of the twelfth month, they rested.

After that, they celebrated a feast each year on the fourteenth and fifteenth day of the last month. This feast is called the feast of Purim, and to this day the Jews celebrate it every year.

Esther accuses Haman at her banquet

The big fish casts Jonah up on the shore

35

The story of Jonah and the big fish

IN BIBLICAL TIMES, THE CITY of Nineveh was a great metropolis. It was in the country of Assyria.

In the city of Nineveh there were beautiful temples, and large palaces, and many houses. It was a big city, and thousands of people lived there.

Walls a hundred feet high encircled Nineveh, and they were wide and thick enough so that three horse-drawn chariots could drive around on top of the walls, side by side. Fifteen hundred towers, each one two hundred feet high, were built above the walls. From these towers guardsmen could shoot their arrows at any approaching enemy.

Nineveh was a rich and beautiful city, but the people who lived there were wicked and the Lord determined to punish them. Before He did so, however, He wanted to warn them and give them a chance to repent of their sins.

The Lord chose a man named Jonah to go and tell the people of Nineveh about the punishment they were sure to suffer for their sins. When He spoke to Jonah, however, Jonah was afraid to go; and Jonah thought he could escape from the command of the Lord by running away. He fled to a seaport not far from Jerusalem and booked passage on a ship that would take him to a far-distant land.

After Jonah's ship had sailed out to sea, the Lord caused a violent windstorm to sweep across the waters, and the ship was in grave danger of being broken to pieces. The sailors were all frightened and prayed in terror to the various idols they worshiped. They threw part of the cargo overboard, trying to make the ship lighter, but still the ship appeared to be in serious trouble and the storm continued to rage.

A great storm comes up and threatens the boat in which Jonah travels.

Everyone on board was frightened except Jonah. Jonah was asleep in the ship's cabin and did not even know there was a storm blowing. At length the captain of the ship went to where Jonah was sleeping and awakened him.

"How can you lie there sleeping when the ship is almost ready to break in pieces?" the captain demanded. "Get up and pray to your God. Perhaps He can save us!"

Jonah and the ship's captain returned to where the other men of the crew were talking.

"Someone on board has sinned wickedly," said one of the men. "This storm has been sent because of him."

Jonah is thrown into the water

"Let's cast lots and find out which one of us is the sinner," said another man. They all felt certain that this was a sure way to determine which man was responsible for the trouble, and this time it proved to be the case, for the lot fell to Jonah.

"Who are you?" they asked him. "What terrible thing have you done to bring this storm upon us?"

"I am a Hebrew," Jonah answered. "I am running away from the voice of the God who made all things—the earth, the sea, and the sky, and all the people of the earth."

"Why are you running away from the voice of your God?" they asked wonderingly. "And what can we do with you, so that this dreadful storm will stop before we are all killed?"

"Throw me overboard, and the waters will be calm for you as soon as you are rid of me," said Jonah. "I know very well that this danger has come to you only because I am here."

The sailors did not want to throw Jonah into the sea, and they rowed hard, trying to reach land, but the storm was too strong and they had to give up. They still dreaded the idea of throwing Jonah to what seemed certain death by drowning, and they all prayed to the Lord for forgiveness.

"Please do not punish us for what we must do," they prayed. "If you have sent the storm because of him, then we must cast him overboard."

No sooner had Jonah been thrown into the sea than the storm stopped and the waters were calm.

A big fish swallows Jonah God did not intend that Jonah should drown. He had sent a great fish alongside the ship, to swallow Jonah as he hit the water. Jonah remained inside the fish for three days and three nights. During that time he prayed constantly to the Lord and repented of his wrongdoing in trying to flee from the voice of the Lord.

God heard Jonah's prayers and caused the fish to cast Jonah out on the dry land by the seaside. Then God again commanded Jonah to visit Nineveh and warn the people of God's intention to punish them for their wickedness. This time Jonah obeyed.

Nineveh was such a large place that a man could walk for three days in going from one end to the other of the city. Jonah waited until he had walked within the city for one full day, and then he made the proclamation God had commanded him to make.

"Nineveh is to be destroyed in forty days," he called out in a loud voice. "Nineveh will be destroyed because of the people's sins!"

The people of Nineveh were sure that God must have sent Jonah. Immediately they began to mend their ways. They repented of their wickedness and prayed to the Lord for forgiveness.

The big fish casts Jonah up on the shore.

The king of Nineveh issued an order that everyone must fast and pray. "Let everyone turn away from sin and repent," he said. "Perhaps if we are penitent, the Lord will forgive us."

Jonah preaches to the people of Nineveh and prophesies their destruction.

Throughout the city, then the people obeyed the king's decree and prayed humbly for the Lord's pardon. God saw their changed ways and heard their prayers. He did not destroy the city because it was not evil any more.

This angered Jonah.

"I am shamed before all these people," he exclaimed. "I told them that the Lord was going to destroy them all after forty days, and my prophecy did not come true! I was afraid this would happen, because I knew all along that the Lord is merciful. As for me, I would be better off dead now. I wish the Lord would let me die!"

The Lord spoke kindly to Jonah, in spite of the fact that Jonah was guilty of an unforgiving spirit and should not have said such things.

Jonah could not bear to remain in Nineveh. He went outside of the city to stay for a while, so that he might be near enough to see what happened there. He built himself a booth, or shelter, and sat under it in the shade.

The Lord made a large vine grow up over Jonah's booth in a single day,

Jonah retires under the miraculous tree and his heart is softened.

to give him ample shade, and to keep him cool in the heat of the day. Jonah was very grateful for that vine. He did not know that it was just part of a lesson God intended.

The day after the vine had grown up over Jonah's booth, God sent a worm to gnaw at the vine and make it wilt. Then God caused a hot east wind to blow, and made the sun burn down on Jonah's head until he was overcome by the dreadful heat.

Once again Jonah cried out that he would be better off dead.

The Lord then showed Jonah how the vine had been intended as a lesson to him.

If Jonah felt sorry about the destruction of the vine, which had grown in a single day, should not the Lord feel even more sorry at the thought of destroying a great city that had been built for years, along with thousands of innocent babies and helpless animals? This was the lesson that the Lord gave Jonah.

Jonah understood then, and was ashamed.

36

The story of Tobias and his journey

THE BIBLE WAS TRANSLATED INTO LATIN nearly sixteen hundred years ago by St. Jerome, one of the great scholars of ancient Rome. St. Jerome's translation is called the Vulgate, which means that it was written in the language of the people (of Rome).

There were fourteen books or parts of books that St. Jerome called the Apocrypha, meaning the "hidden, or secret, books." The famous English translation called the King James version, which was published in 1611, included the Apocrypha; but most editions of the King James version printed in the last hundred years have not included them. Catholics include eleven of Apocrypha's fourteen books and sections as inspired and sacred parts of the Bible.

The Apocrypha are part of the Old Testament, and like the Old Testament as a whole they include some poetry, some history, some stories of the adventures or experiences of people who were faithful to God, some prayers, and some prophecy. Included are three sections in the book of Daniel and six chapters in the book of Esther. Others are:

THE BOOK OF TOBIAS and THE BOOK OF JUDITH, about which you can read on the following pages.

THE BOOK OF WISDOM, also called THE WISDOM OF SOLOMON, which is a book of moral and religious advice, following the Proverbs.

ECCLESIASTICUS, also called THE WISDOM OF JESUS (or JESHUA) THE SON OF SIRACH, another book of advice.

THE BOOK OF BARUCH, a book of prophecy and prayer, written by a friend or follower of the prophet Jeremiah.

Two books of history, covering a period just before the Christian era, when a family named the Maccabees or Machabees ruled over the Jewish people.

The three other sections Of the other parts of the Apocrypha, which are not accepted as inspired, two are additional books of Esdras or Ezra (which are simply different ways of spelling the same name). They tell more about the rebuilding of the Temple of Jesusalem, about which you can read on pages 485 to 501.

Finally there is the Prayer of Manasseh. The Bible does mention a prayer made by a Jewish king of that name, but this is not accepted as being the same prayer.

Tobias and his troubles Tobias was an Israelite, a descendant of Naphtali, one of the sons of Jacob who founded the Twelve Tribes of Israel. Tobias lived almost three thousand years ago, at the time when the wicked King Ahab was ruling in the kingdom of Israel.

At that time Ahab often fought wars against the kings of Assyria, and in these wars the kings of Assyria would often capture Jewish people. Tobias was captured in this way and taken to the Assyrian capital, Nineveh. Captives with him were his wife and his young son, whom he had named Tobias also—we would call the boy Tobias, Jr.

Most of the Jewish people who were captured worshiped the idols of the Assyrians and disobeyed other commandments of God, but Tobias and his family continued to worship God only and obey His laws.

For some time Tobias prospered. At one time he was so prosperous that he deposited ten talents of silver—worth at least ten thousand dollars—with a man named Gabael, a banker in the city of Rhagae or Rages, about 350 or 400 miles away from Nineveh.

But then Tobias's troubles started. Because he buried his kinsmen when they died, and burial was against the laws of the Assyrians, the king of Assyria sent men to arrest him. Tobias fled from the city, and the king seized all his property. Later Tobias was able to return to Nineveh, but he became blind and could not earn a living, so the family lived on a small amount that Tobias's wife earned and they were very poor. Tobias was very unhappy, and he prayed to God for help.

The prayers of Tobias and Sara

On the same day that Tobias was praying, another prayer was being offered up to God by a faithful but unfortunate young woman in a far-off town called Ecbatana.

The young woman's name was Sara. She was the daughter of an Israelite named Raguel, who like Tobias was a captive far from home but had continued to worship and obey God. Sara was a good and religious girl, but she was the victim of a wicked demon named Asmodeus. Seven times Sara had been married, but every time Asmodeus had killed her new husband immediately after the ceremony, so she had never been able even to begin married life with any one of the seven. She too prayed piously to God for help against this demon. People were beginning to think she murdered all her husbands!

God heard both prayers, Tobias's and Sara's, and He sent the angel Raphael to earth to help them both.

Just at this time, no doubt through inspiration sent by God, Tobias remembered the large amount of money he had left with Gabael. If he could get that money he and his family would not be poor any more. So he called his son to him.

By this time young Tobias had grown almost to full manhood. He was old enough to marry and old enough to make the long journey to Rhagae. His father told him about the money.

"Go to Rhagae and collect the money," old Tobias told his son. "Hire a man to go with you and I will pay him wages."

Young Tobias dutifully went out to look for a man, and of course the first man he found was Raphael. He could not know Raphael was an angel, and Raphael said his name was Azariah and that he was an Israelite, a kinsman of Tobias; he had in truth taken the appearance and person of the real Azariah, for the purpose of this mission. Old Tobias was delighted with this choice of a companion for his son, and soon the disguised angel and the young man set out together for Rhagae.

When the two travelers came to the great river Tigris, young Tobias

Raphael (standing) tells Tobias to save parts of the fish. A Doré engraving.

went to the bank of the river to wash himself and a big fish leaped out of the water and attacked him. Tobias was frightened and cried, "Help! Help me!" but the angel calmly said,

"Take hold of the fish and pull it on shore."

Tobias did this and was surprised to find it easy. He and Raphael made a meal of the fish. Then Raphael said,

"Now cut out the heart, the liver and the gall bladder of the fish and keep them."

Tobias did this, but he soon became curious and asked,

"Azariah, what are these parts of the fish for?"

"If you are troubled by an evil spirit," Raphael replied, "burn the heart and liver and the smoke will drive the spirit away. As for the gall bladder, that will cure blindness."

Tobias and Sara are Married
After a few days the travelers came to the city of Ecbatana, which lay on the road from Nineveh to Rhagae, about halfway between them. Here they stayed with Raguel (for he was of the same people and religion), and Tobias fell in love with Sara; but he was afraid to marry her because he had heard about her seven previous husbands, all of whom had immediately died.

"Don't be afraid," Raphael told him. "When you take your wife to the bridal chamber, put some hot ashes on the heart and liver of the fish, to make smoke. And you and your wife must both pray, and God will save you."

Then Raphael spoke, as representative of old Tobias, to Raguel, the father of Sara, for that is how marriages were arranged in those times. Raguel was delighted and gladly gave his daughter to young Tobias, and they were married almost at once; but Raguel still feared that this new son-in-law would die like all the others. He even dug a grave to put Tobias in.

Sara was even more frightened, and cried. But when she and Tobias went to their room, Tobias made the smoke and they both prayed, as Raphael had told them to, and the demon fled far away; but Raphael, using his supernatural powers, followed him and bound him so that he could do no more damage.

The next morning Raguel sent a maid to the room of the newly wedded couple, fully expecting to find Tobias dead. When he heard that Tobias was still alive he was so happy that he arranged for two weeks of feasting. While this was going on, Raphael went alone to the city of Rhagae and collected the ten talents of silver, which he brought back to young Tobias. Then all three of them went back to Nineveh.

Raphael Before they arrived, Raphael told young Tobias,
reveals "Remember to have the gall of the fish in your hand and
himself put it on your father's eyes."

Old Tobias was so happy to have his son home safely,
with a new wife, that he wept; and while he was weeping
young Tobias put the gall on his eyes and the old man rubbed them and
rubbed away the film that had made him blind.

They still did not know that Raphael was an angel, but they were so
grateful to the man they called Azariah that old Tobias offered him half
of the money he had brought back. But Raphael said,

"Do not pay me anything. Instead, give thanks to God. For I am the
angel Raphael, whom God sent to help you."

Then they fell on their knees and praised God. Raphael disappeared,
and neither old nor young Tobias ever had need of his help again, for they
lived good lives and long lives.

37

The story of Judith and Holofernes

 UDITH WAS a beautiful and pious woman of Bethulia, a city of the Jews, who saved her city from an army of Assyrian invaders.

The Assyrians were commanded by a general named Holofernes. He had a fearsome army, and he had already conquered several parts of the Jews' land of Judea, together with several surrounding lands. All the people were terrified, and although they prayed to God to save them they lost their faith that even the Lord could overcome such a great army.

Now, Judith had been a widow for more than three years, for her husband had died of a sunstroke during the harvest; and Judith had worn rough clothing and had not made herself seem attractive, because she was in mourning. But when her city was threatened she left her house and went to the leaders of the city, at the head of whom was a man named Uzziah, and she said to them,

"You can be beaten only if you lose faith in the Lord; for He can do anything. Tonight I will go out from the city, and with the Lord's help I will save the city."

Ussiah and the other elders, or leading citizens, were so desperate that they were happy to do anything that might save them. They said to Judith,

"Go, then, and may the Lord be with you."

Judith made herself very beautiful, with fine clothes and jewelry and perfumes. Then she prayed to God for help. And then, taking her maid with her, she went to the gates of the city (for in those times all cities were protected by great walls and gates).

Judith was so beautiful that Uzziah and the other elders gasped with admiration when they saw her. They opened the gates and Judith went fearlessly to the camp of the enemy army. There she asked to see the commander, Holofernes, and because of her beauty and her apparent wealth she was taken to him at once.

To Holofernes and the other Assyrians, Judith said that she had left the city of the Jews because she did not wish to be destroyed with its other people. They believed this, and that night she was invited to a banquet given by Holofernes.

Judith would not eat the food offered her by Holofernes, because the Jews had very strict religious laws concerning the foods they could eat and the way it must be prepared. Instead, Judith ate food that she had brought with her and that her maid served to her.

"But you will soon run out of food," said Holofernes, "and then what can we give you to eat?"

"My food will last as long as you live, my lord," Judith answered; but

Judith enters the tent of Holofernes.

Judith carries the head of Holofernes back to her city, to prove his death.

Holofernes did not understand her meaning. He thought she meant that God would continue to provide her with food.

For four days, Judith lived in the camp of the Assyrians while they prepared to attack the city of Bethulia. Each day Judith prayed to the Lord, and each night she ate her own food at the banquet of Holofernes.

On the fourth night all the other guests left early, so that Judith was alone with Holofernes. She took a sword, prayed to God for strength, and cut off his head. Then with her maid she returned to Bethulia.

When the Assyrians found that their commander had been killed, they first believed that the Israelites had been able to attack them; and this caused such fear among them that they fled from the valley in which lay Bethulia, and the city was saved.

Judith was a great heroine among the people of her city, and her success caused them once again to have faith in God to save them from their enemies.

38

The story of Susanna and the Elders

THE PROPHET DANIEL PROVED WHEN HE WAS still a very young man, little more than a boy, that he had great wisdom and also was blessed with God's favor.

In Babylon, the city to which Daniel had been taken by King Nebuchadnezzar (as told in Story 26), there lived a beautiful young woman named Susanna. She was good as well as beautiful, and she was fortunate besides in being married to a rich man, whose name was Joakim.

Among the Jewish people living in Babylon were two elders who were greatly respected by the people and who had been appointed judges. In reality these elders were not good but wicked men. They wanted power over Susanna, and together they went to her and threatened her.

"If you do not submit to us," they told her, "we will tell all the people that we saw you meet another man in your garden, which would be unfaithful to your husband Joakim."

Susanna was in despair. "There is no hope for me, even though I am innocent," she said, groaning; "for the people will surely believe these men, who are elders and judges, instead of me." Nevertheless she was both courageous and good and she refused to submit to the elders.

The elders carried out their threat. They accused Susanna of misbehavior, and though Susanna denied it the people believed the elders.

At this point God caused Daniel to feel the holy spirit that was in him, and Daniel came to the defense of Susanna.

"You have condemned this woman without a fair trial," he told the people.

So great was Daniel's reputation for wisdom that the people gladly listened to him and did what he asked. Daniel asked only that he be able to question the two elders—not when the elders were together but when they were apart. The people agreed and separated the elders so that neither could hear what the other said.

To the first, Daniel said,

"When you saw this woman in the garden with the strange man, what kind of tree were they under?"

"A mastic tree," the elder replied.

Then Daniel had the first elder sent away and called the other to him.

"Under what kind of tree did you see them?" he asked again.

"Under a liveoak tree," the second elder replied.

As Daniel had supposed, the elders had not gone so far in their false story as to agree on small details.

After this, the people could not think evil of Susanna. She was declared innocent and Daniel was highly praised.

Daniel speaks, Susanna is set free, and the elders are bound instead.

39

The story of Bel and the Dragon

NOTHER OF THE ADDED PARTS of the book of Daniel tells how Daniel outwitted the priests of one idol, or false god, and destroyed another false god.

This happened when Daniel had become a great and famous man. Cyrus, one of the most famous kings of ancient history, was king in Babylon at that time and he liked and trusted Daniel more than any of his other courtiers and advisers.

The Babylonians, including the king, worshiped idols. Daniel worshiped only God. Also, he knew that the idols were false gods, merely statues and not gods at all.

The chief god of the Babylonians was called Bel. He was served by priests, and every day they took to him many bushels of flour for bread, and forty sheep for meat, and a full cask of wine for drink. The king and the people of Babylon believed that the god Bel actually ate and drank this much daily.

One day the king said to Daniel, "Why don't you worship Bel, as we do?"

"He is only an idol," Daniel replied. "I worship only the living God, Lord of heaven and earth."

"How can you say Bel is not a living god?" the king asked. "Just think of what he eats and drinks every day!"

At this Daniel laughed. "He never ate anything," Daniel assured the king. "He is only clay inside and bronze outside."

This made the king angry. He wanted to believe in Bel, but he trusted Daniel also. He called the priests to Bel to him and said,

"You must prove to me that Bel actually eats the food you supply to him. If you cannot prove it, you will die; but if you can prove it, Daniel must die."

The priests—there were seventy of them—agreed to this, and so did Daniel. They all went to the big room of the temple in which the statue of Bel stood, and the priests put the food and drink on the table before Bel. Then the priests left. The king intended to seal up the room so that no one could possibly get in or out without breaking the seal. Before leaving the room, Daniel and his servants scattered fine ashes on the floor around the table and the statue.

Then Daniel left the room, and the king sealed it, and they went home.

Of course, there was a secret entrance to the room, known to the priests and to no one else. Every night the priests and their wives and children went into the temple by the secret entrance and had their dinner from the food that had been put there for Bel.

Footprints in the ashes The next morning the king went back to the temple, attended by Daniel. First the king satisfied himself that no one could have tampered with the seals he put on the doors. Then he broke the seals and opened the doors. All the food and wine was gone from the table!

The king was convinced. "You are great, O Bel!" he cried.

But Daniel laughed. "Look at the footprints," he said.

The king looked. "I see footprints of men, women, and children!" he exclaimed.

It did not take long for the king to find the secret door. So the priests were killed and Bel was destroyed. But the king still worshiped idols.

The king also worshiped an enormous serpent, or snake, that was kept in the temple. It was probably nothing more than a boa constrictor or python, one of the giant snakes that we often read about today, but in that part of the country such big snakes were not known and the people called it a dragon and thought it must be a god.

"You cannot deny that this is a *living* god," the king said to Daniel.

"I do not deny that it is living," Daniel replied; "but one cannot kill God, while I can kill this serpent easily."

"You have my permission to try," said the king.

Daniel made a concoction of pitch and fat and hairs and fed it to the big snake. The concoction swelled up inside the snake until it burst and died.

This convinced the king, but the people were so angry that they forced the king to have Daniel put in a den of lions. There were seven lions in the den and they were given no food, but God did not let them touch Daniel, and God even sent the prophet Habakkuk to take food to Daniel in the lions' den.

Daniel remained in the lions' den nearly a week. On the seventh day the king came to the lions' den. Actually he intended to mourn for Daniel, who had been his friend. It did not occur to him that Daniel might still be alive. But Daniel sat calmly in the den. He was not even hungry.

Finally the king was convinced. He acknowledged the greatness of God and Daniel was again the most favored and most powerful man in Babylon.

In Story 29 you can read how Daniel was placed in a lions' den under another king, Darius, and came to no harm because he had God's protection.

Daniel (bending over) shows the king the footprints.

40

The story of the three guardsmen

HE TWO APOCRYPHAL BOOKS OF ESDRAS tell more about how the Temple was rebuilt at Jerusalem, about five hundred years before Jesus was born, and they tell how a young man named Zerubbabel won the favor of the mighty Persian king Darius and became the governor of Jerusalem.

At that time Jerusalem was ruled by the Persian empire. Jerusalem had been conquered and destroyed more than fifty years before and most of the Jewish people had been taken as captives to Babylon and other places in the Persian empire. But even while these Jewish people were not allowed to return to their homeland (for fear they would again become strong and be able to make war against the Persians), they were permitted to live in comparative freedom and several of them rose to high positions in the governments of the Persian kings. Young men of Jewish families were educated and trained for positions of leadership the same as young men of other nationalities.

In the second year of his reign, Darius gave a great feast in his capital city of Nineveh and invited the governors of all the many provinces in his vast empire.

One night during the period in which the feast was under way (for such a great occasion might last for weeks), Darius was sleeping in his room. Outside his door, to guard him, were three young men of his bodyguard. One of these young men was Zerubbabel, a member of a noble Jewish family.

The three young bodyguards, who had to be awake all night, decided to take a problem and see who could answer it best; and they agreed to show their answers to Darius and ask him to reward the wisest of them.

Esdras (or Ezra) praying while the Temple at Jerusalem is being rebuilt.

The question they selected was, "What is the strongest of all things?"
The first guardsman wrote, "Wine is strongest." The second wrote, "The
king is strongest." The third, who was Zerubbabel, wrote, "Women are

Assembly of the Jews in the capital of Darius, to hear Zerubbabel speak.

strongest; but truth is mighty and will prevail"—that is, the truth can conquer anything.

All three placed their written answers under the king's pillow, so that he would see them when he awoke. When Darius did awake and read the answers he assembled all his governors and famous guests and then he summoned the three young guardsmen.

"Now," said Darius to the guardsmen, "explain to us why you answered as you did."

The first to speak, the young man who had answered "Wine," said,

"Wine is strongest because it affects men's minds and makes them think things are not as they actually are. If wine is stronger than men's minds, it must be stronger than men themselves."

Next to speak was the guardsman who had answered, "The king." He said,

"Surely men are strongest of all things on earth, since they rule the land and the sea and all things on them; and since the king is master of all men, the king must be the strongest of all things."

Now it was Zerubbabel's turn to speak.

"Women are more powerful than men," said Zerubbabel, "because no matter how powerful a man is, he will let himself be influenced by the woman he loves. This is true even of the king himself.

"But even more powerful than women is truth. For nothing can change truth. Wine cannot change it, men cannot change it, the king cannot change it, women cannot change it. Truth never dies; it lives forever. No man can dispute with truth. Blessed be the God of truth!"

Then all the assembled rulers shouted, "Yes, truth is the strongest!" And Darius said to Zerubbabel, "You have won and have proved yourself wisest. Sit next to me, and you shall be called my kinsman, and whatever favor you ask of me I will grant."

At once Zerubbabel asked as his favor that the city of Jerusalem should be rebuilt (for at that time Jerusalem still lay in ruins), and that the treasures takes from Jerusalem should be restored to it.

Darius rose, and kissed Zerubbabel, and gave orders that Zerubbabel should be escorted safely to Jerusalem and that all the governors of all the provinces should give him supplies and other help in rebuilding the city.

Soon afterward, Zerubbabel assembled a large group of Jews who had been living in exile in Persia, the country of Darius; and Zerubbabel led his group back to Jerusalem, where they rebuilt the city.

41

The story of the Maccabees

F OR MORE THAN FIVE HUNDRED YEARS, the Jewish people were ruled by foreign kings. During only one period of about one hundred years did they have kings of their own. These kings were members of a family called the Maccabees.

You will remember that the Jews had been made subject to the kings of Persia—such great kings as Cyrus and Darius. But about three hundred years before Jesus was born, an even greater king arose in Greece. He was called Alexander the Great, and he conquered not only the Persians but nearly all the civilized world that was then known to the people who lived near the Mediterranean Sea. But Alexander respected the religions of other peoples and did not destroy Jerusalem or the Temple as other conquerors had done. The Jews willingly paid taxes to Alexander and many of them joined Alexander's army and fought for him.

Unfortunately, Alexander died when he was a very young man and the kings who came after him were not so favorable toward the Jews and their religion. Under these later kings, the Jewish people entered a long period of great suffering.

It is true that for a time the Jews continued to be faithful to God and God continued to protect them. When one of the great kings, Seleucus, sent a general named Heliodorus to destroy Jerusalem and the Temple, God sent His angels to beat Heliodorus until he was unable to carry out his purpose and the city was spared. But a later king named Antiochus did destroy Jerusalem and ruin the Temple, and also he persecuted those who still worshiped God and obeyed his laws. Many faithful Jews became martyrs, or men who suffer and die for their faith.

The martyrdom of Eleazar.

One of these martyrs was a priest, Eleazar. He was beaten to death because he would not eat pork (for it was then a religious law of the Jews, and is still a religious law with many Jews, that pork may not be eaten).

Even more horrible was the death of seven sons and their mother. One by one, each of the sons was offered a choice: He could eat the flesh of swine (that is, pork), and go free; or he could refuse, in which case he would be tortured to death. One by one the seven young men refused, and one by one they were put to death, each time with all the surviving brothers and their mother watching. Many of the tortures were too cruel to describe. The seventh and last son was the bravest of all—not only because he had seen all six of his brothers tortured and knew what would happen to him if he refused, but also because he was offered a very important position as a nobleman if he would desert God and serve Antiochus. Nevertheless he refused and was killed, and then his mother (who had urged him not to submit to the king) was also put to death.

When this persecution of the Jews began, a young Jewish leader named Judas Maccabeus, with eight or nine followers, fled to the mountains and

The martyrdom of the seven brothers before their mother.

lived there. They lived "in the manner of beasts," eating what food they could find and sleeping in the open. Judas Maccabeus was the son of a rich and noble priest named Mattathias. This priest had five sons, of whom Judas was the third oldest. Because Mattathias was so influential among the Jews, the cruel king Antiochus offered him great wealth and power in return for submission, but Mattathias refused and led a revolt against Antiochus. The revolt did not succeed, but neither was it wholly beaten down; and when old Mattathias died he had a large body of followers who were willing to fight the armies of Antiochus.

On the death of his father, Judas Maccabeus (which means "Judas the Hammerer") came out of hiding and became the leader of the Jewish army.

Judas was a brilliant military leader, and in addition he was a devout man. Before every battle he and his entire army prayed to God, and fasted as a sign of worship. Once Judas led his army of only six thousand men against an army of forty-seven thousand and won a great victory. He attacked several cities that had been captured by the Syrian armies of Antiochus, and he recaptured and freed these cities. By the time he was

Judas Maccabeus restores the services in the Temple.

ready to recapture Jerusalem, his enemies were so afraid of him that they retreated and he marched into Jerusalem without opposition.

Judas Maccabeus was so successful that his enemies had no choice but to make peace with him. Judea, the land of the Jews, became an independent country with Judas Maccabeus as its king; and though Judas was killed in battle only two or three years later, his brothers and then their sons and grandsons and descendants were kings over Judea for a hundred years. These were the Maccabee kings.

But finally the Roman Empire became so powerful that no nation was able to withstand it; and about sixty years before Jesus was born, after a hundred years of Maccabee rulers, Judea along with all nearby countries became mere provinces of Rome. After that time there never was an independent nation of the Jewish people until the modern state of Israel was founded.

Pronunciation of Names

The following list includes all proper names used in this volume. The names are pronounced in two ways. First, the name is spelled exactly as it appears in the text, with the pronunciation shown by the following method:

The acute accent (′) is used to denote the accented syllables; the un-accented syllables are separated by a dot (·). Compound proper names are indicated by a dash (–).

VOWEL SOUNDS

ā as in Ā′bĕl, nāme
ē as in Ē′sạu, bēat
ī as in Ī′răd, tīme
ō as in Ō′bĕd, bōne
ū as in Ū′rĭ·el, mūle
ȳ as in Tȳre, mȳ

ă as in Băb′ȳ·lon, hăt
ĕ as in Bĕn′ja·mĭn, mĕn
ĭ as in Gĭl′e·ăd, sĭn
ŏ as in Nŏd, tŏp
ŭ as in Lŭz, bŭt
ў as in O·lўm′pas, hўmn

ȧ as in Ȧ·bī′ȧ, ȧbout
ė as in Tė·kō′ȧ, rėsult

ĩ as in ĩ·dụ·mē′ȧ, Ĩdiot
ŏ as in Ŏ·zī′as,fŏment

â as in Shâ′ron, pârent
á as in Shē′bá, sofá
ä as in Är′nŏn, fär
ạ as in Sạul, fạll

ē̦ as in Ăb′nēr, stērn
ī̦ as in Ō′phĭr, stĭr
ô as in Ā′chôr, môre
û as in Ûr, mûrder
ụ as in Ăb′i·shụr, fụr
ụ as in Shụ′ȧ, rụde

CONSONANT SOUNDS

ḡ as in Gē′zēr, ḡet
x (gs) as in Ăl·ĕx·ăn′dēr, example
ç as in Çȳ′prus, fançy

ġ as in Ġĕn′tīleṣ, enġine
ṣ (z) as in Jewṣ, amuṣe

After the name is pronounced according to the table above, it is re-spelled in syllables that show the pronunciation by a different (and, for some persons, an easier) method.

Ȧ·bĕd′ne·gō	uh·BED·nuh·go	Är·tăx·ērx′ĕṣ	are·tuck·ZERK·zeez
Ȧ·bī′a·thär	uh·BY·uh·thar	Ā′sá	A·suh
Ȧ·bī′jah	uh·BY·juh	Ăth·a·lī′ah	ath·uh·LIE·uh
Ȧ·bĭm′e·lĕch	uh·BIM·uh·leck	Ăz·a·rī′ah	az·uh·RYE·uh
Ăb′sa·lŏm	AB·suh·lum	Bā′al	BAY·ul
Ăd·o·nī′jah	add·uh·NIGH·juh	Bā′a·shá	BAY·uh·shuh
Ā′hăb	A·hab	Băb′ȳ·lon	BAB·ih·lon
Ȧ·hăṣ·ū·ē′rus	uh·haz·you·EE·rus	Bā′rụch	BAY·rook
Ȧ·hā′vá	uh·HAY·vuh	Băth′shĕ·bá	BATH·sheh·buh
Ā′hăz	A·haz	Bĕl·shăz′zar	bell·SHAZ·er
Ȧ·ha·zī′ah	ay·huh·ZYE·uh	Bĕl·te·shăz′zar	bell·teh·SHAZ·er
Ȧ·hī′jah	uh·HIGH·juh	Bĕn·hā′dăd	ben·HAY·dad
Ăl·ĕx·ăn′dēr	al·eg·ZAN·der	Bĕn′ja·mĭn	BEN·juh·min
Ăm·a·zī′ah	am·uh·ZYE·uh	Bĕth′el	BETH·uhl
Ăm′mŏn	AM·mahn	Bĕth·ụ·lī′á	beth·you·LIE·uh
Ā′mŏs	A·muss	Cā′năan	KAY·nun
Ăn·tī′o·chus	an·TIE·uh·kus	Cär′mel	CAR·mel
Ā′phek	A·feck	Chăl·dē′an	kal·DEE·un

Chē′bär	KEY·bar	Lĕb′a·non	LEB·uh·nun
Çȳ′rus	SIGH·rus	Lē′vīte	LEE·vite
Dă·măs′cus	duh·MASS·kus	Mā′a·chah	MAY·uh·kuh
Dăn	DAN	Măc′ca·beeş	MACK·uh·beez
Dăn′iel	DAN·yul	Măc·ca·bē′us	mack·uh·BEE·us
Dā·rī′us	duh·RYE·us	Mal′a·chi	MAL·uh·kye
Dā′vid	DAY·vid	Mā·năs′seh	muh·NASS·uh
Dō′than	DOH·thun	Măt·ta·thī′as	mat·uh·THIGH·us
Ē′dom	EE·dum	Mēde	MEED
Ē′gўpt	EE·jipt	Mĕn′a·hĕm	MEN·uh·hem
Ē′lah	EE·luh	Mē′shach	ME·shack
Ē·le·ā′zar	ee·lee·A·zer	Mī′cah	MY·kuh
Ē·lī′jah	ee·LYE·juh	Mī·cā′iah	my·KAY·uh
Ē·lī′sha	ee·LYE·shuh	Mĭr′ĭ·am	MIR·ee·um
Ē′phră·ĭm	EE·fruh·im	Mĭsh′a·el	MISH·ay·el
Ĕs′dras	EZ·drus	Mĭz′peh	MIZ·peh
Ĕs′thĕr	ESS·ter	Mō′ab	MOH·ab
Ē·zē′ki·el	ee·ZEE·kee·el	Mŏr′de·cāi	MORE·deh·kye
Ĕz′rā	EZ·ruh	Mō′şeş	MOH·zuz
Gā′brĭ·el	GAY·bree·ul	Nā′a·man	NAY·uh·mun
Gĕd·a·lī′ah	ged·uh·LYE·uh	Nā′bŏth	NAY·buth
Gē·hā′zī	ghee·HAY·zye	Nā′dab	NAY·dab
Gĭd′e·on	GID·ee·un	Nā′hum	NAY·hum
Gī′hon	GUY·hon	Nā′than	NAY·thun
Gĭl′găl	GILL·gal	Nĕ′băt	NEE·bat
Gō·lī′ath	guh·LYE·uth	Nĕb·u·chad·nĕz′zar	neb·uh·cud·NEZ·er
Hăb′ăk·kŭk	HAB·uh·kuk	Nē·he·mī′ah	nee·heh·MY·uh
Hă·dăs′sah	huh·DASS·uh	Nín′e·veh	NIN·eh·vuh
Hăg′ga·ī	HAG·uh·eye	Ō·ba·dī′ah	oh·buh·DYE·uh
Hā′man	HAY·mun	Ŏm′rī	OM·rye
Hăn·a·nī′ah	han·uh·NIGH·uh	Pē′kah	PEE·kuh
Hăz′a·el	HAZ·uh·el	Pĕk·a·hī′ah	peck·uh·HIGH·uh
Hē′brew	HEE·brew	Pē·nü′el	peh·NEW·ul
Hĕz·e·kī′ah	hez·uh·KYE·uh	Phā′raōh	FAIR·oh
Hī′ram	HIGH·rum	Phăr′ĭ·see	FAIR·ih·see
Hĭt′tīte	HIT·ite	Phĭ·lĭs′tĭne	fih·LISS·tin
Hŏl·o·fēr′nĕs	hol·uh·FUR·neez	Pŭl	PUHL
Hō′reb	HO·reb	Pū′rim	PURE·im
Hŏ·sē′á	ho·ZEE·uh	Rā′moth·gĭl′e·ăd	RAY·moth·GILL·ee·ad
Hŏ·shē′á	ho·SHE·uh	Rē·ho·bō′am	ree·hoh·BOH·um
Hŭl′dah	HULL·duh	Să·mā′rĭ·á	suh·MAY·ree·uh
Ī·sā′iah	eye·ZAY·uh	Săn·băl′lat	san·BAL·ut
Ĭsh′ma·el	ISH·may·el	Se·leu′cus	seh·LOO·kus
Ĭş′rael	IZ·ray·el	Sĕn·năch′e·rĭb	sen·NACK·uh·rib
Ĭs′sa·char	ISS·uh·car	Shā′drach	SHAY·drack
Jĕ·hō′a·hăz	gee·HO·uh·haz	Shă′lum	SHALL·um
Jĕ·hō′ăsh	gee·HO·ash	Shē′bá	SHE·buh
Jĕ·hoi′a·chĭn	gee·HOI·uh·kin	Shē′chem	SHEE·kum
Jĕ·hoi′a·dá	gee·HOI·uh·duh	Shĕm·a·ī′ah	shem·uh·EYE·uh
Jĕ·hoi′a·kĭm	gee·HOI·uh·kim	Shī′lōh	SHY·loh
Jĕ·hō′ram	gee·HO·rum	Shĭm′e·ī	SHIM·ee·eye
Jĕ·hŏsh′a·phăt	gee·HOSH·uh·fat	Shĭ′shăk	SHY·shack
Jĕ′hū	GEE·hew	Shụ′nem	SHOO·num
Jĕr·e·mī′ah	jair·uh·MY·uh	Shụ′shan	SHOO·shan
Jĕr′ĭ·chō	JAIR·uh·koh	Si·do′ni·an	sih·DOH·nee·un
Jĕr·o·bō′am	jair·uh·BOH·um	Sŏl′o·mon	SOL·uh·mun
Jĕ·rụ′să·lĕm	jeh·ROO·suh·lem	Tĭb′nī	TIB·nigh
Jĕsh′u·á	JESH·you·uh	Tĭg′lath·pĭ·lē′şer	TIG·lath·pih·LEE·zer
Jĕz′e·bĕl	JEZ·uh·bell	Tō·bī′ah	tuh·BY·uh
Jĕz′re·el	JEZ·ree·el	Tȳre	TIRE
Jō′ăb	JOH·ab	Ŭz′	UHZ
Jō′ăsh	JOH·ash	Ŭz·zī′ah	uh·ZYE·uh
Jōb	JOHB	Văsh′tī	VASH·tie
Jō′el	JOH·ul	Zăch·a·rī′ah	zack·uh·RYE·uh
Jō′nah	JOH·nuh	Zăr′e·phăth	ZARE·eh·fath
Jôr′dan	JORE·dun	Zĕch·a·rī′ah	zeck·uh·RYE·uh
Jŏ·sī′ah	joh·SIGH·uh	Zĕd·e·kī′ah	zed·eh·KYE·uh
Jō′tham	JOH·tham	Zĕph·e·nī′ah	zef·uh·NIGH·uh
Jū′dah	JOO·duh	Zē′rah	ZEE·ruh
Jū′das	JOO·dus	Zĕr·u·ī′ah	zair·you·EYE·uh
Jū·dē′á	joo·DEE·uh	Zē·rŭb′ba·bĕl	zuh·RUB·uh·bell
Jū′dith	JOO·dith	Zĭm′rī	ZIM·rye